A NEW DIRECTION

A Cognitive-Behavioral Treatment Curriculum

LONG-TERM WORKBOOK

Socialization

Mapping a Life
of Recovery & Freedom
for Chemically Dependent
Criminal Offenders

**A Collaboration of Chemical Dependency Professionals from
the Minnesota Department of Corrections and the Hazelden Foundation**

HAZELDEN®

Hazelden
Center City, Minnesota 55012-0176

1-800-328-9000
1-651-213-4590 (Fax)
www.hazelden.org

ISBN: 1-56838-849-7

Cover design by David Spohn
Interior design by Terri Kinne
Illustrations by Patrice Barton

Hazelden Publishing and Educational Services is a division of the Hazelden Foundation, a not-for-profit organization. Since 1949, Hazelden has been a leader in promoting the dignity and treatment of people afflicted with the disease of chemical dependency.

The mission of the foundation is to improve the quality of life for individuals, families, and communities by providing a national continuum of information, education, and recovery services that are widely accessible; to advance the field through research and training; and to improve our quality and effectiveness through continuous improvement and innovation.

Stemming from that, the mission of this division is to provide quality information and support to people wherever they may be in their personal journey—from education and early intervention, through treatment and recovery, to personal and spiritual growth.

The headquarters of the Hazelden Foundation are in Center City, Minnesota. Additional treatment facilities are located in Chicago, Illinois; New York, New York; Plymouth, Minnesota; St. Paul, Minnesota; and West Palm Beach, Florida. At these sites, we provide a continuum of care for men and women of all ages. Our Plymouth facility is designed specifically for youth and families.

For more information on Hazelden, please call **1-800-257-7800.** Or you may access our World Wide Web site on the Internet at **www.hazelden.org.**

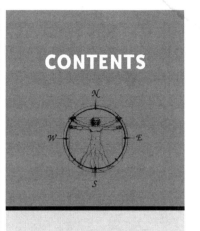

CONTENTS

**A NEW
DIRECTION**

*A Cognitive-Behavioral
Treatment Curriculum*

Acknowledgments

Thanks to all who have contributed to this curriculum:

Sheryl Ramstad Hvass
Commissioner, Minnesota Department of Corrections

Peter Bell
Executive Vice President, Hazelden Publishing and Educational Services

James D. Kaul, Ph.D.
Director, TRIAD Chemical Dependency Program
Minnesota Department of Corrections

Will Alexander
Sex Offender/Chemical Dependency Services Unit, Minnesota Department of Corrections

Minnesota Department of Corrections

Sex Offender Treatment Program at Lino Lakes Minnesota Correctional Facility

> Robin Goldman, Director
> Jim Berg, Program Supervisor
> Brian Heinsohn, Corrections Program Therapist
> Greg Kraft, Corrections Program Therapist
> K. Kaprice Borowski Krebsbach, Corrections Program Therapist
> Kevin Nelson, Corrections Program Therapist
> Tim Schrupp, Corrections Program Therapist
> Pamela Stanchfield, Corrections Program Therapist
> Jason Terwey, Corrections Program Therapist
> John Vieno, Corrections Program Therapist
> Cynthia Woodward, Corrections Program Therapist

TRIAD Chemical Dependency Program at Lino Lakes Minnesota Correctional Facility

> Launie Zaffke, Supervisor
> Randy Tenge, Supervisor
> Carmen Ihlenfeldt, Acting Supervisor
> Thomas A. Berner, Corrections Program Therapist
> Toni Brezina, Corrections Program Therapist
> Jeanie Cook, Corrections Program Therapist
> Ronald J. DeGidio, Corrections Program Therapist
> Susan DeGidio, Corrections Program Therapist
> Maryann Edgerley, Corrections Program Therapist
> Connie Garritsen, Corrections Program Therapist
> Gerald Gibcke, Corrections Program Therapist
> Anthony Hoheisel, Corrections Program Therapist
> Deidra Jones, Corrections Program Therapist
> Beth Matchey, Corrections Program Therapist
> Jack McGee, Corrections Program Therapist
> Jackie Michaelson, Corrections Program Therapist

Hal Palmer, Corrections Program Therapist
Terrance Peach, Corrections Program Therapist
Holly Petersen, Corrections Program Therapist
Linda Rose, Corrections Program Therapist
Kathy Thompson, Corrections Program Therapist
Beverly Welo, Corrections Program Therapist

Reshape Chemical Dependency Program at Saint Cloud Minnesota Correctional Facility

Robert L. Jungbauer, Director
Christine Fortson, Corrections Program Therapist
Tracanne Nelson, Corrections Program Therapist
Jeffrey D. Spies, Corrections Program Therapist

Atlantis Chemical Dependency Program at Stillwater Minnesota Correctional Facility

Bob Reed, Director
Dennis Abitz, Corrections Program Therapist
Bill Burgin, Corrections Program Therapist
Tom Shipp, Corrections Program Therapist

New Dimensions Chemical Dependency Program at Faribault Minnesota Correctional Facility

Michael Coleman, Supervisor
Michele Caron, Corrections Program Therapist

Central Office

Jim Linehan, Corrections Program Therapist

Minnesota Department of Corrections Supervising Agents

Russ Stricker, Correctional Unit Supervisor
Bobbi Chevaliar-Jones, Intensive Supervised Release Agent
William Hafner, Corrections Agent
Gregory Fletcher, 180 Degrees Halfway House

In Addition:

Writers: Corrine Casanova, Deborah Johnson, Stephen Lehman, Joseph M. Moriarity, Paul Schersten.
Designer: Terri Kinne. **Typesetters:** Terri Kinne, Julie Szamocki. **Illustrator:** Patrice Barton.
Prepress: Don Freeman, Kathryn Kjorlien, Rachelle Kuehl, Joan Seim, Tracy Snyder, David Spohn.
Editor: Corrine Casanova. **Copy editors:** Monica Dwyer Abress, Kristal Leebrick, Caryn Pernu.
Proofreaders: Catherine Broberg, Kristal Leebrick. **Marketer:** Michelle Samlaska. **Video production manager:** Alexis Scott.

Special thanks: Any Color Painting Company; Blue Moon Production Company; Eden Re-entry Services; inmates and staff of Lino Lakes, Rush City, and Stillwater Minnesota Correctional Facilities.

Special thanks to Hazelden: Nancy Alliegro, Derrick Crim, Joe Fittipaldi, Carole Kilpela, Nick Motu, Karin Nord, Patricia Owen, Rebecca Post, Teri Ryan, Ann Standing, Sue Thill, and Kris VanHoof-Haines.

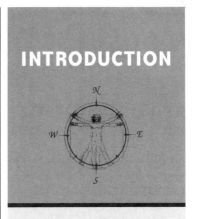

Socialization

The word *socialization* can be a bit confusing and intimidating. You might not even be sure of the meaning. School kids learn about socialization in a class called social studies.

Here, you will learn about how different cultures and people from various backgrounds and parts of the world get along.

You may or may not remember learning about other cultures. Maybe you weren't interested. That's fine. By participating in this program, you've been given another chance to learn about others. In doing so, you'll be learning about yourself—what makes you the way you are and how you relate to others. Most adult relationships involve give-and-take. This workbook will show you why it's not okay to be a taker in life all the time. It's important to give back. To do this, you need to learn how to *socialize* with others in the world in a positive way.

Socialization is really about you and me. It's how you treat yourself and others. It's all about having relationships and getting along with others. This entire workbook was created to track where you've been, how you got there, what works in your life and what doesn't work, and how to make changes in your life. Step-by-step you'll be given instructions on how to change your thinking and behavior. You've been given a chance at a fresh new life. It'll involve some work though.

In studying socialization, you'll learn about how to have healthy relationships, manage your anger, and what impact your actions have on others. These are all important tools in your recovery from crime and alcohol and other drugs. A crime-free and drug-free life will bring you freedom. It's possible, but it takes hard work, support, and a plan.

You won't be able to do it alone.
You must reach out to others, and
this won't be easy.

Socialize

Socialize means to find companionship with others, mingle with others, and take part in social activities in a positive way.

Chances are, you've hurt people who have tried to help you. Maybe they don't trust you anymore. So, you'll need to work on relationship building. You've spent years tearing down these relationships; now it's time to rebuild them. Or, maybe you'll need to let some of them go. We'll help you do that. You'll also need to find new healthy support systems. We'll help you find ways to do that, too.

Thinking and Behavior Patterns

We'll take a hard look at what you've done in the past and how it has affected others. We'll point out destructive patterns of behavior and thinking that keep recurring in your life. These patterns are not unique to addicts and criminals. Everyone creates and repeats patterns of thinking and behaving.

We will discuss two types of **thinking patterns**: criminal thinking patterns and addictive thinking patterns. Criminal thinking patterns are the types of thoughts that say it is okay to violate others or their property. Examples would be

- "I found myself in a situation."
- "I'd rather be doing time than be straight like you."
- "I punched him because he had no right to look at me that way."

Addictive thinking patterns are the types of thoughts that say you can continue using alcohol and other drugs no matter what the cost to yourself or others. Addictive thinking patterns overlap with criminal thinking patterns. The two reinforce and drive each other.

> **Thinking Patterns**
>
> *Thinking patterns* are habits of thought that a person uses so often they just seem to come naturally.

Examples of addictive thinking patterns would be

- "I can quit whenever I want."
- "My problem isn't drinking, it's my wife's nagging."
- "Nothing ever works out. I deserve to get high."

■

Criminality and addiction are both, to a large degree, *thinking* problems before they lead to *behavior* problems. Our **behavior patterns** will change based on the changes in our thinking patterns.

As a criminal and an addict, you have developed both criminal and addictive thinking patterns. These thinking patterns don't influence all the thoughts you have, but they may dominate your thinking. This leads to trouble. The good news is that you can change your patterns of thinking with a little help and a lot of effort.

You also need to pay attention to what leads you to use alcohol and other drugs. If you recognize your behaviors early enough, you can take action and stop the behavior before you do something you'll really regret: relapse.

You can plan ways to substitute new, positive, supportive behaviors for negative ones. This will help you avoid relapse.

Behavior Patterns

Behavior patterns are habits of behavior that a person uses so often they just seem to come naturally.

Each of you has a unique background and your own story to tell. You'll have a chance to tell that story and, in the process, replace some old, worn-out behaviors with new, healthy ones. Many people have been successful in programs such as this. They've made the commitment to positive change. Are you motivated to change? You have to want to change in order for any of this to work. Are you ready? Read on!

"We're ready to change!"

"You know what? If you want to join the rest of the world not in prison, then you have to take control of your thinking and your life."

— Ahmed A., former offender, Minnesota

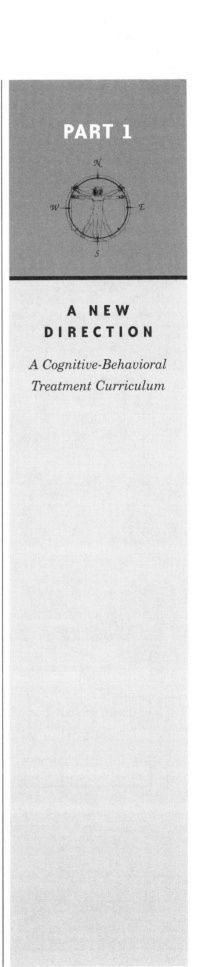

Where Have I Been?

It's important to know where you've been and how you got to where you are today. You may have been brought up in a family where things appeared to work out. Or maybe you come from a family in which no one worked, no one paid the bills, or no one seemed to care.

You may have had a more difficult childhood than anyone else on the cell block, but you are all at the same place now. You're incarcerated. You can't change the past. Unless you make some changes in your thinking and behavior now, you may well end up behind bars again after you have been released. That's the reality. The good news is that the future doesn't have to repeat the past. A bright future is just around the corner, but first you must be willing to take some chances and make some real changes in your thinking and actions.

Throughout this program, you'll have the chance to hear from two very different guys, Jim and Jack. Their lives started out very different, but they ended up at the same place: addicted and incarcerated. They are now both participants in this *New Direction* curriculum, just like you. They are working on the same stuff as you will be. On the next page, Jim tells his story first.

It's in the Genes: Things You Cannot Change

Maybe you come from a long line of alcoholics. Your mom was a drunk, your grandpa was a drunk, your uncle was a drunk, and the list goes on and on. Recent research proves that heredity is a factor in who will become addicted to alcohol and other drugs. You can't change that.

Your <u>genes</u> may influence whether you have a substance abuse problem. This is not, however, an excuse for drinking and using.

There are things in your life that you can't change no matter how hard you try. For example, Jim can't change the way he grew up. Others can't change the fact that their mothers were chronic alcoholics who drank throughout their pregnancy. These people may now have ***fetal alcohol syndrome,*** and they'll always have problems as a result.

Genes

Genes are compounds expressed as physical traits in your body. You inherit a set of genes from your parents.

Jim's Story

I'm twenty-five years old. I'm doing time in a maximum security prison. I'm in a drug rehab program now. Things are looking better and better. But it wasn't that way always.

My life didn't start out so good. I never knew my dad. Actually, I don't think my mom really had a clue who he was. There were so many men coming over and "taking care" of us. My mom wasn't around much when I became old enough to take care of the other kids. We lived on the south side of Chicago. Since I was the oldest of my five brothers, I had to take care of them. Some days we'd have food while other times we had nothing. We'd get kicked out of our apartment and end up at a shelter. I liked it when we ended up at the shelter 'cause at least we had a roof over our head, blankets, warm food, and a bed. But this never lasted long. Mom would find someone else for us to live with. Another "uncle" would come to the rescue. This really sucked. I had nobody to turn to. Drinking beer seemed to help, even though I was only nine years old. We switched schools all the time. I knew I needed to make some money and I couldn't wait 'til I was old enough to work. Besides, we needed some serious cash. I got tired of waiting for another "uncle" to save us. I knew some guys who had everything: the nice car, cash, and women. Everyone respected them. This was their turf. They saw I was down-and-out. At first, they bought me cans of Coke and candy once in a while from the corner store. Then they'd ask me to have a beer with them. I liked that. I felt like I belonged. They took care of me. They'd give me sacks of McDonald's burgers and fries to bring home to the rest of my brothers. Soon, I was getting cash if I'd just deliver this bag to someone over by school. It was easy enough. It was no big deal, and these guys really needed me. They told me I was helping them out. And they were there to protect me. They became my only friends. Soon, I was taking money and dealing drugs. It happened so fast. I almost didn't see it happening.

— Jim R.,
serving time for dealing drugs and manslaughter

It's not all bad news though. People with fetal alcohol syndrome can manage this limitation just like they can manage being hearing impaired or losing their eyesight or the use of their legs. They can still have lives they can be proud of. They have control of how they want to deal with this limitation. They have choices, and so do you.

Maybe you have a mental illness or diabetes. You can't change that. There's nothing you can do about that, but you can deal with it responsibly. Take your prescription medications as directed by your medical doctor. This can make a big difference in how you deal with and see the real world. You aren't helpless. In fact, only you hold the power to change your thinking and behavior. Nobody else can do it for you.

Let's look at the bigger picture. When we look back on our lives, we see how we came to believe what we believe and value. It all starts with culture.

Culture

Your nationality describes what country you were born in. Your ethnic background describes what country or countries your ancestors came from. Ethnic cultures are often passed on from generation to generation, regardless of nationality. Your nationality may be American and your ethnic background Vietnamese. Being part of an ethnic culture adds another dimension to your value system. The exercise on the next page will help you explain how you learned certain values and attitudes.

Your Culture

This exercise is designed to highlight some of your unique experiences that you have learned because of the way you were raised. Answer honestly.

➤ What is your ethnic background? For example, what country or countries did your family come from?

_____

_____

_____

➤ What occasions do you celebrate that your friends don't?

_____

_____

_____

➤ Do you remember any family traditions? An example could be gathering with family and eating turkey for Thanksgiving.

_____

_____

_____

Being part of an ethnic culture adds another dimension to your value system.

➤ What foods does your family traditionally eat?

_____

_____

_____

➤ What does your family do for fun? Go to movies, play sports, play games, watch TV, worship together, listen to music?

_____

_____

_____

➤ How do you treat your elders? Does the younger generation expect to take care of the older generation?

_____

_____

_____

➤ Does your culture listen to special music? If so, what kind?

_____

_____

_____

➤ Does your family encourage going to school? If so, how?

_____

_____

_____

➤ How does your culture view drinking alcohol and using other drugs?

_____

_____

_____

We Are Family

Everyone is born into some kind of community. An advantage of belonging to a community is the support you can receive from its members. A *family* is considered part of this community.

Families are like individuals. They have both strengths and weaknesses. In healthy, strong families, members have common goals, respect each other's boundaries, and understand the expectations of being a member of that family. This is accomplished with open and honest communication.

Family

A *family* is a system, or unit, that is made up of a number of individuals. Some of these people are related by blood, others are not. Whether they live with you or not, they have the ability to affect and influence you.

Unhealthy families have more weaknesses than strengths. Their lack of common goals and unclear boundaries create instability. Rules may be rigid or change from day to day. Or there might not be any rules at all. Family members may not understand what is expected of them. Family members may feel alienated and are often unmotivated to take on responsibilities.

Families are not 100 percent healthy or unhealthy. They are somewhere in between. Understanding your family's strengths and weaknesses will help you see how you came to be who you are. While it's important to recognize your family's strengths, the focus in treatment is often on weaknesses. You may question this. Think of it this way: When you go to the emergency room for a broken left arm, the doctor doesn't spend time examining your right arm. You're there to fix your broken left arm. Treatment is the same way. We're here to help you fix what's broken, not what's working.

It's time to learn more about where you came from. Looking at your family history will help you understand some of the reasons why you are the way you are. Keep in mind that things like addictive and destructive behaviors tend to run in families. Patterns develop in families and often repeat themselves through the generations.

Looking Back at Your Family History

Genealogy research is very popular in our culture. You may even know people who are into that. People like to explore where they came from—where they have their roots. It shows that they belong to a group of people with the same last name or heritage. We're going to ask you to complete a genealogy chart, commonly referred to as a family tree.

EXERCISE 2 EXERCISE

What's Your Family History?

➤ A family tree closely resembles an actual tree, so let's use that as an example. The branches of your tree will contain the names of people you are related to. To start with, place your name on the bottom of the tree trunk on page 16. Then add your birth date and where you were born.

Jim's Story

Yeah, I didn't want to do this family exercise at first. It seemed like too much work. Besides, I didn't care who the hell was in my family. I don't even know who my dad is. I never will know that either. So, I did this family tree thing a little different than the other guys. I just put my "uncle" at the time as my father. It worked out fine. I still learned a lot about my family even though they weren't always blood relatives. Turns out my grandpa served time behind bars, too. So did my ma for minor crap. My ma's brothers did some time, too. What a coincidence, huh? Give it a try. You don't need to do it perfect. Just do the best you can with the information you have.

— Jim R.,
serving time for dealing drugs and manslaughter

Father's Parents

_____

_____

↓

Father

_____

Mother's Parents

_____

_____

↓

Mother

_____

↓

Brothers and Sisters

_____

_____

_____

_____

_____

_____

Your Name: _____

Date of Birth: _____

Place of Birth: _____

Now, fill in the spaces provided with the other members of your family. The branches at the top of the tree represent your grandparents. The large branches directly underneath represent your parents. The smaller branches represent your brothers and sisters.

We'll refer back to this exercise at the end of part 1, so it is important that you complete it as best you can.

➤ In the space provided below, write down the names of your family members. Start with immediate family members, such as mother, father, sisters, and brothers. Then, go out a little further. Do you know who your grandparents are? Write down their names. Do you know whether your mother or father has any brothers or sisters? Write their names down. Do your aunts and uncles have any kids? Write their names down. Next to each person's name, write his or her relationship to you. This list is just to get you started.

Person   Relationship to You

_____

_____

_____

_____

_____

_____

_____

_____

Person	Relationship to You

➤ Now it's time to place all these people on the genealogy chart on page 19. Write your name on the bottom of the chart and work your way to the top. Start filling in the blanks on the genealogy chart and add circles or squares where you need to according to the instructions below.

☐   Use a square for males.

○   Use a circle for females.

—   Connect people who are married with a line.

—//—   If the people are not married, but are living together, use a line with slashes through it.

X   If a person died, place an "X" through the shape.

➤ Researching your family may involve making phone calls and writing letters to other family members. You may also ask family members to do some research on the computer if they have access to the World Wide Web.

➤ Write each person's birth date under his or her shape (if you know it).

GENEALOGY CHART

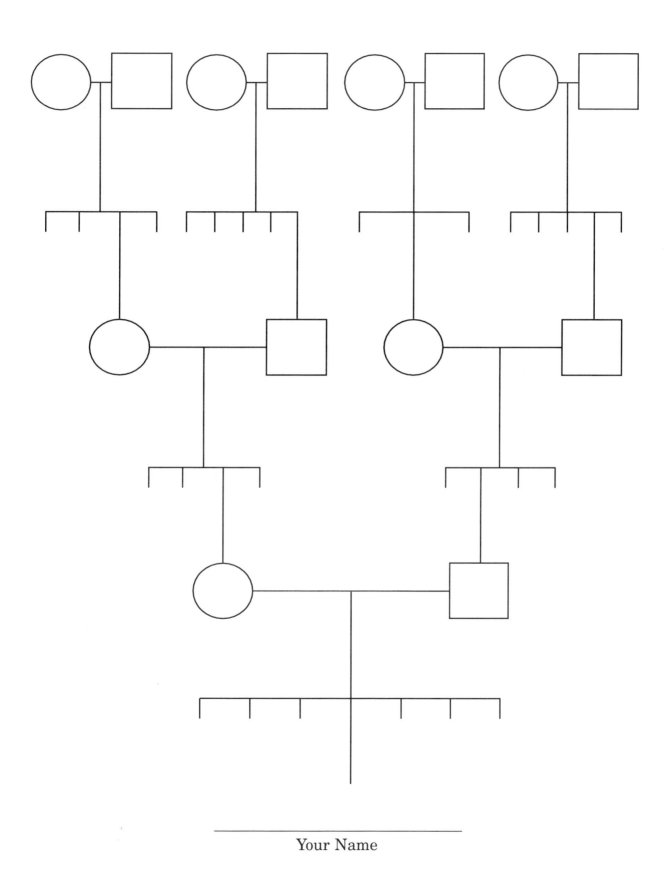

Your Name

➤ Place the initials of the corresponding characteristics inside the shape that represents each person. For example, Jim's grandfather would have a CR in his square because he has been incarcerated. Try to limit yourself to one or two characteristics for each person.

CA	=	Caring
CD	=	Chemically dependent
CR	=	Has been incarcerated
D	=	Disability of some kind
ED	=	Well-educated
EM	=	Problems dealing with emotions
H	=	Happy person
NG	=	Negative role model
N	=	Nurturing
NE	=	Little or no education
P	=	Poor, has little of monetary value
PR	=	Positive role model
S	=	Smart, intelligent
SX	=	Sexual offender
TX	=	Enrolled in alcohol/drug treatment program
V	=	Violent

Complete your genealogy chart the best you can in the time that you have. (You may complete a more detailed version on a separate piece of paper later.) Group members will discuss their family histories and what they've learned. Through research, some of you may have found out things about your family that you didn't know before.

Exploring Your Family History

Answer the questions in this exercise as best you can. You may not be able to answer all of them because you may never have had contact with some family members. That's why we've given you at least three choices for each section of the exercise. If you never met your father and don't have a stepfather, you might want to think of a male role model when completing this exercise. This could be an uncle, grandfather, or neighbor.

Section 1

To answer the following questions, circle one of the people listed below:

father   **stepfather**   **male role model**

➤ If you have selected a role model, who is this person?

_____

➤ Write down three positive qualities of the person you chose.

1. _____

2. _____

3. _____

➤ Write down three negative qualities of the person you chose.

1. _____

2. _____

3. _____

➤ How do you feel about this person today? Be specific.

_____

_____

_____

➤ How do you and this person communicate? Examples of ways some people might communicate include

• We don't talk when we're upset with each other. If I'm angry at him, I will do something destructive, like take his car and crash it.

• We yell and scream. We get violent.

• We sit down and talk calmly about what's bothering us.

_____

_____

_____

➤ What are some of the best times you have had with this person?

_____

_____

➤ What are some of the worst times you have had with this person?

_____

_____

Section 2

To answer the following questions, circle one of the people listed below:

mother   **stepmother**   **female role model**

➤ If you have selected a role model, who is this person?

_____

➤ Write down three positive qualities of the person you chose.

1. _____

2. _____

3. _____

➤ Write down three negative qualities of the person you chose.

1. _____

2. _____

3. _____

➤ How do you feel about this person today? Be specific.

_____

_____

_____

➤ How did you and this person communicate?

_____

_____

_____

_____

➤ What are some of the best times you have had with this person?

_____

_____

➤ What are some of the worst times you have had with this person?

_____

_____

➤ You are now going to make a line graph that relates to your relationships with the people you chose on pages 21 and 23. This is from when you were born to now. For example, 0-5 is from when you were born to age 5. How close did you feel to them? Ask this question for each age bracket and place a dot above that corresponds to distant, close, or very close. Use a square for the male person you chose, and a circle for the female person you chose.

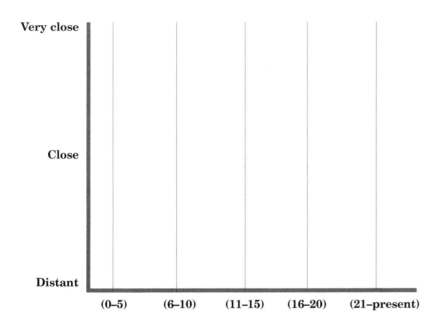

What made each relationship close?

_____

_____

What made each relationship distant?

_____

_____

▶ Take a look at the positive and negative qualities in the lists below. Circle five qualities about yourself from the positive column and five from the negative column.

POSITIVE	NEGATIVE
Caring	Bitter
Compassionate	Controlling
Confident	Cowardly
Dependable	Cruel
Forgiving	Dishonest
Friendly	Hateful
Honest	Hopeless
Loyal	Impatient
Motivated	Moody
Powerful	Resentful
Secure	Rough
Sincere	Rude
Smart	Uninterested
Spiritual	Weak
Strong	
Trustworthy	

➤ Look at the ten words you circled. Can you use those same words to describe the people listed below? If so, write the appropriate word next to each person.

1. Your father | stepfather | male role model:

   _____

2. Your mother | stepmother | female role model:

   _____

3. Your significant other:

   _____

4. Your closest sibling:

   _____

5. Your best friend:

   _____

By completing exercise 3, you've learned a little more about your family history. Now it's time to focus on you. Have you ever heard about someone writing a memoir? This is also referred to as an ***autobiography***. It doesn't matter what your age or situation, it's never too early to start telling your story. The questions in exercise 4 will help provide information for your life's story. But you won't actually write your life story until the end of part 1. When you do so, you'll refer back to this exercise.

> **Autobiography**
>
> An *autobiography* is the story a person writes about his or her own life.

Helping You to Write Your Life's Story

Answer the following questions as best you can. To do this, you will need to think back and revisit some childhood memories. The purpose of this exercise is to teach you more about yourself and where you came from. Answer as honestly as possible. If a question doesn't apply to you, leave it blank.

➤ 1. What is your date of birth?

_____

➤ 2. Who named you? Why was that name chosen?

_____

_____

_____

_____

➤ 3. Give the names and birth dates of your siblings.

Name	Birth Date
_____	_____
_____	_____
_____	_____
_____	_____
_____	_____

➤ 4. Where did you live while growing up?

_____

_____

_____

➤ 5. What kind of work did your mom and dad do?

_____

_____

_____

➤ 6. Was your family religious? (check one)

_____ Yes   _____ No

➤ 7. What is your earliest childhood memory?

_____

_____

_____

➤ 8. What was it like being a small child in your home?

_____

_____

Did you feel safe? (check one)

_____ Yes   _____ No

9. When you were a small child, who was special to you?

_____

_____

10. When you were a small child, who seemed to care most about you?

_____

_____

11. How would you describe your place or role in your family?

_____

_____

_____

_____

How would you describe your place or role in your family?

12. How did your parents treat each of their children?

_____

_____

_____

13. Who disciplined you?

_____

_____

How were you disciplined?

_____

_____

Why were you disciplined in that manner?

_____

_____

How did you feel about the discipline you received?

_____

_____

➤ 14. What feeling was shown in your family most often?
(circle one)

      Anger   Fear

      Love   Hurt

➤ 15. How did your parents seem to get along?

_____

_____

What did they enjoy together?

_____

_____

What did they fight about?

_____

_____

How did they fight?

_____

_____

➤ 16. What effect do you think your parents' relationship had on you as a child?

_____

_____

_____

What effect do you think your parents' relationship has had on you as an adult?

_____

_____

_____

➤ 17. What was your earliest sexual experience?

_____

_____

_____

When did you learn about sex? From whom?

_____

_____

➤ 18. How did you feel about going to school?

_____

_____

_____

What did you like about school?

_____

_____

_____

What didn't you like about school?

_____

_____

_____

Who were your friends at school?

_____

_____

_____

What subjects were difficult for you?

_____

_____

_____

➤ 19. Were there any changes in your living arrangements or family during your grade school, middle school, and high school years? If so, what were they?

_____

_____

_____

➤ 20. What friends and activities were you involved with during high school years?

_____

_____

_____

➤ 21. What were your successes during your high school years?

_____

_____

_____

What were your failures?

_____

_____

_____

➤ 22. Who did you want to be like in grade school?

_____

_____

In middle school?

_____

_____

In high school?

_____

_____

➤ 23. What was your chemical use in grade school?

_____

_____

_____

What friends and activities were you involved with during high school years?

In middle school?

_____

_____

_____

In high school?

_____

_____

_____

➤ 24. Were you involved in any schooling or training beyond high school?

_____

_____

_____

_____

➤ 25. What kind of jobs have you held? Next to each job, write down how long you worked at each job.

_____

_____

_____

_____

_____

_____

_____

_____

➤ 26. Have you ever been married or been in a committed relationship? (check one)

_____ Yes   _____ No

➤ 27. Do you have children? If so, how many? What are their ages?

_____

_____

_____

_____

_____

➤ 28. How has your chemical use affected your life as an adult?

_____

_____

_____

_____

_____

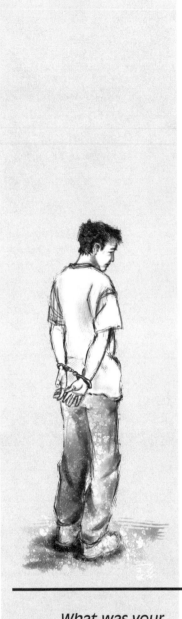

What was your situation leading up to your most recent offense?

29. When and how did you first get involved in illegal activities? Was it something you felt everyone in the family was expected to do?

_____

_____

_____

_____

30. Are you the first person in your family to be incarcerated? (check one)

_____ Yes   _____ No

31. What behaviors have you been arrested for? When?

_____

_____

_____

_____

32. What was your situation leading up to your most recent offense?

_____

_____

_____

_____

➤ 33. How has your alcohol and other drug use affected
your illegal behavior?

_____

_____

_____

_____

➤ 34. What efforts have you made in the past to change and
control your behavior? Efforts might include treatment
programs, support groups, or willpower.

_____

_____

_____

_____

➤ 35. What recovery programs have you or your family
been involved in?

_____

_____

_____

_____

Early Chemical Use

Research shows that children who grow up in families where there is chemical abuse are at greater risk to become dependent on or abuse chemicals. Research also shows that physical or sexual abuse in childhood is directly linked to adult behavior of physical or sexual abuse of others.

Throughout life, many people struggle with feelings of shame. You may feel hopeless, helpless, inadequate, and disgusted with yourself. You may have a difficult time developing healthy boundaries and finding intimacy. The list goes on and on.

**To get beyond shame,
we must first see it, own it,
and then move on.**

You cannot change the fact that you are part of a family of criminals, or have a mom who was a crack addict, or were born to someone who never wanted you. Your childhood experiences may have put you at *high risk* for leading a life of crime and becoming an addict, but they didn't guarantee it. There are plenty of stories of people who had extremely difficult childhoods and, as a result, became more determined than most to lead healthy, loving, and nurturing lives. On the other hand, many people who had extremely difficult childhoods choose to live a life of crime—like Jim, whose story we first read on page 9. Maybe you had a very different story. Maybe your family seemed to function effectively. But still you chose a life of crime and drinking and drugging. Let's take a look now at the story of Jack.

Children who grow up in families where there is chemical abuse are at greater risk to become dependent on or abuse chemicals.

Jack's Story

I'm thirty-four years old. I'm in a medium-security prison. Now that I'm in this drug rehab program, I'm learning a lot about myself. I think I'm going to make it this time.

My life should have been great. I shouldn't have struggled and screwed up. But I did. I wanted to prove I could do it myself. My dad was always on my case. My mom stayed home with us kids asking what we were up to, making fresh-baked cookies, and pouring big tall glasses of milk. Honest to god. It was like some kind of Brady Bunch episode. I was so bored with my life. I wanted to live on the edge. I wanted more. As a teen, I finally found that excitement. A group of guys in school used to cut classes and hang out in one guy's house because his mom was always at work. That worked out good. We'd crash out there for hours and then find older kids to cruise around town with. Money was never a problem. So we'd always be able to find someone to get us some beer or a little weed. Cutting classes became a big issue with my parents. They began to make a bunch of rules for me at home. I'd blow them off. I didn't care. I just always felt like I didn't belong with my family. This new group of friends made me feel like I belonged. They always asked me to go with them 'cause they knew I had the cash. Things got out of hand though—and fast. We got busted a couple of times for underage drinking. The thing is once I started drinking, I never wanted to stop. When I was drunk, I finally felt like I belonged. Without some kind of high, I was out of my mind. I was so frustrated with everything. I felt hopeless. Nothing was going to save me until I scored again. I was smart enough. I just didn't apply myself to school. All that mattered was getting high and pissing off my parents. I didn't know there was hope. Being hopeless was just how I was. I was used to it.

— Jack S.,
serving time for dealing drugs and aggravated robbery

Both Jim and Jack chose a life of crime and abusing alcohol and other drugs, even though they came from very different backgrounds. Your family has a direct influence on how you view yourself and the world, but no matter what that influence is, *you make your own choices.* Think of other people who grew up like you did and did not choose to become criminals. Realize that some people have it tougher than others, but there is always someone who had it worse than you did who chose to live a responsible life. You have choices today that will allow you to turn your life around. Setting boundaries is an important first step in doing this.

Boundaries

Imagine your body with an invisible shield around it. It's your **boundary** from the outside world. Only you can decide where your boundaries begin and end. For example, you might not feel comfortable talking to a stranger positioned just six inches from your face. This stranger would be too close. You'd step back. However, your boundary would be in a different place for your partner or spouse. You might even move closer. Think about what your boundaries were like when you were growing up. Were they clear or a bit confusing? Understand that we're not just talking about physical boundaries here. Closeness and distance also relate to emotional boundaries.

You may have boundaries that don't allow anyone in. These are called "too close" boundaries. You fence yourself in and say things like "I don't want any relationship. It's not worth the pain." "Too distant" boundaries are when you allow everyone in. You don't even know what your boundaries are, and you aren't able to tell others what they are. As a result, your boundaries are continually violated.

Boundary

A *boundary* is like a line that shows where something begins and something ends.

**Boundaries
have a purpose.
They help define
who we are.**

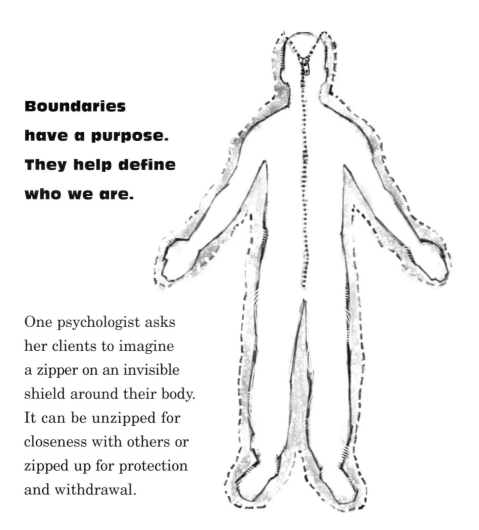

One psychologist asks her clients to imagine a zipper on an invisible shield around their body. It can be unzipped for closeness with others or zipped up for protection and withdrawal.

People who have grown up in addicted and abusive families often are confused about their boundaries. They might have been physically, sexually, or emotionally assaulted at a young age. Maybe they were told they were stupid and should do something they weren't comfortable doing. They may have never known it was okay to set their own boundaries.

We learn to respect ourselves by setting limits with others. Healthy people have flexible boundaries. They can develop intimacy and closeness in relationships when that is appropriate. Likewise, they can be more distant when the situation or relationship calls for that. It's now time to look at the boundaries you have.

What Are Your Boundaries?

This exercise is all about boundaries. It is not designed to decide whether your boundaries are healthy or unhealthy. The idea is to realize that we all have boundaries. Let's take a look at how we formed our boundaries. Answer the following questions in the spaces provided.

➤ What kind of boundaries did you have with your friends? Did you let them tell you how you should act? Did you let them push you around? Or did you always let them know who was in charge?

_____

_____

_____

_____

_____

➤ What kind of boundaries did you have with your family while you were growing up? For example, was there a lot of affection or hate between family members? How did they express their feelings?

_____

_____

_____

"Good fences make good neighbors."
— Robert Frost

_____

_____

_____

_____

➤ How did you build your boundaries? Did someone teach you, or did you just kind of figure it out on your own? For example, maybe your mom told you not to trust strangers. Or maybe she told you to always do what you are told even if you are uncomfortable and don't think it is right.

_____

_____

_____

_____

_____

_____

What kind of boundaries did you have with your family while you were growing up?

Healthy and unhealthy boundaries will be fully explored in part 3 of this workbook. Boundaries and intimacy are closely related topics. Let's take a look now at how you learned about intimacy.

Intimacy

Say the word **_intimacy_** and what's the first word that pops into your head? _Sex,_ right? Ultimately, it can involve sex, but it's really much more than that. Advertisements typically use sex to try to sell us things. Alcohol ads may promote the idea that the more we drink, the more fun we'll have. If we just take that one drink, suddenly we'll be much more relaxed, accepted by others, and good things will happen to us. The problem is that one drink is too many and too much is never enough. It's important that we become aware of temptations. By drinking a beer, we aren't suddenly going to have that woman on the television screen drooling over us. It just doesn't happen that way.

> **Intimacy**
>
> _Intimacy_ means being emotionally connected and close through a variety of activities that are informal, deep, and personal. To be intimate, people need to be able to honestly and respectfully share their thoughts and feelings. To be intimate, a sexual relationship is not required.

EXERCISE 6 EXERCISE

The Definition of Intimacy

➤ What does the word _intimacy_ mean to you? Explain in the space provided below.

_____

_____

_____

_____

_____

Belonging

Belonging, or being accepted, is something we want. Belonging is something we do almost without thinking about it. Have you ever felt like you belonged? Maybe you felt it at a neighborhood store when the clerk recognized you and asked you how you were doing. Maybe you were at the post office and you saw a neighbor who knew you. Or maybe you felt it as a child when you received an invitation to a neighbor's birthday party. Belonging is important. That's why chain restaurants like McDonald's are so popular. When you are away from home, you might get homesick and look for places that remind you of home. When you go inside a chain restaurant, you know what to expect and you feel like you're back in your neighborhood.

EXERCISE **7** EXERCISE

Familiar Feelings

➤ When was the last time you felt like you belonged? This might have been a significant moment when someone told you he or she loved you and needed you. It also could have been a time when you were in a place where you felt like you belonged. It might even have been when you were at a basketball game and no one paid attention to you. You simply felt like you belonged because you were all part of a group as you all rooted for the same team.

_____

_____

_____

_____

Looking back on your life, can you honestly say you have felt connected to others? Do you feel you understand what it means to be connected? Being connected doesn't mean using people. If you grew up in an alcoholic family, you may have experienced isolation and loneliness instead of feeling connected. Because of your experiences, you may feel you don't understand intimacy. Maybe an intimate moment in your past meant going up to your room, slamming down a twelve-pack of beer, and then passing out.

Family Rules

In many chemically dependent families, the only connection between other people was a bad connection—being pushed around and yelled at. Many family members might have been continually disrespected and shamed. Were there promises made that were never kept?

EXERCISE **8** EXERCISE

Family Rules: Spoken and Unspoken

➤ What kind of rules did you have in your family, either spoken or unspoken? Write down some of the rules here.

_____

_____

_____

_____

_____

_____

➤ Did everyone in your household have to play by those rules? (check one)

_____ Yes   _____ No

What if someone didn't?

_____

_____

_____

_____

➤ How were women treated in your household?

_____

_____

_____

_____

Did they work? (check one)

_____ Yes   _____ No

Were they caretakers? (check one)

_____ Yes   _____ No

Were they never there? (check one)

_____ Yes   _____ No

➤ Do you see a connection between your family's rules and how you are today? (check one)

_____ Yes   _____ No

If so, how?

_____

_____

_____

_____

_____

_____

Taking an honest look at where you've been will help you understand why you think the way you think.

Taking an honest look at where you've been will help you understand why you think the way you think. You'll need to make some choices and learn to reach out to others who can help you. Connecting with others won't be easy, but it's an essential part of your recovery from alcohol and other drugs—and essential to living a crime-free life.

Shame

Being disrespected all the time, or neglected, or abused sexually may have been part of your childhood. All of this may have created in you intense **shame.** Shame can be devastating. You will have to resolve these issues and heal this pain in order to experience true recovery.

There is growing evidence that shame is at least partly genetic. Certain people may be born with a tendency to develop unhealthy amounts of shame. The kind of shame that adults can relate to starts to develop by age two—right at the time when children start to explore and find a separate identity. Excessive shame delays or distorts this process. The shamed child believes that he has no right to a separate life. He then concludes that he is a weak and flawed person. In turn, he starts to have abandonment issues—feelings of not being loved or wanted and of not belonging. To feel more worthy, he demands excessive attention from others. He does negative things to get this attention.

Shame

Shame is a painful emotion, or way of feeling. It is caused by feelings of guilt, unworthiness, inadequacy, self-disgust, or humiliation.

EXERCISE 9 EXERCISE

Experiencing Shame

➤ Write down three times when you experienced shame during childhood and how you dealt with it each time. Shame is different than guilt. Guilt is "I did a bad thing." Shame is "I am a bad person."

1. _____

_____

2. _____

_____

3. _____

_____

➤ Write down three times when you experienced shame recently and how you dealt with it each time.

1. _____

_____

2. _____

_____

3. _____

_____

We've all experienced some form of shame in our lives. We might have experienced it first with a parent or brother or sister. Calming the shame is difficult, but it is done in many ways. In the past, you most likely dulled the pain with alcohol or other drugs or by having power over others. Today, you need a different approach. Talking about it helps.

Writing Your Autobiography

First, review exercises 2, 3, and 4. By completing these exercises, you have a good start on telling your life's story, or autobiography. After you complete your autobiography, you will be asked to share parts of it with other members of your group. It gives others in your group a chance to learn more about you.

EXERCISE **10** EXERCISE

Your Life's Story, Starring You

To get you started, we'll give you three tips for writing your life's story.

Tip 1

Significant events, both positive and negative, should be included in your life's story. Include your history of alcohol and other drug use and abuse. State your first drinking experience, your first drunk or high, problems in your life caused by your using, periods of sobriety, and how you felt during each of those times.

Tip 2

Start from the earliest memory you have and work your way up to now.

Tip 3

Write a little each day. Your facilitator will let you know when you must complete this assignment. Don't wait until the last minute. By doing a little each day, you'll have time to remember more things for your autobiography.

Writing your life's story is a good way to recognize patterns of behavior and relationships in your life. It's not possible to change your behavior if you don't recognize it in the first place. Change is not easy, but there comes a point in your life when you need to change if you want a different outcome. You simply can't go on the way you have been. If you do, you'll always end up right where you are now: behind bars.

It's now time to look at what works and what doesn't work in your life. We can't make changes and fix things until we know what is broke.

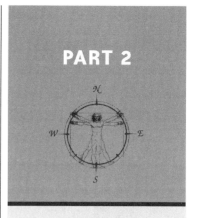

What Works,
What Doesn't?

Finding out where you've been in your life was
the focus in part 1. By completing the exercises in
part 1, you've probably learned something about
your past. Figuring out what works and what
doesn't in your life may seem like a huge job. But
it's not as tricky as you may think. Let's start by
looking at your values.

Values

You learned about your cultural values in part 1 of this workbook. Everyone has some kinds of *values,* but maybe you're not always clear about what your values are. Many people feel that way. Sometimes you act from one set of values, sometimes another. Some of your values support life, self-worth, and good relationships. Other values support pain, abuse, and death.

What are your values? Before you answer that question, let's take a look at the kind of values that most people have: *traditional values.* Those values might be the same as or different from *criminal values.* You see, criminal values are traditional values with a twist. With criminal values, you are only concerned about how things affect you. In the process, other people might get hurt. In fact, you may not even realize that you are hurting someone because you're so focused on yourself.

Values

Values are principles, standards, or qualities by which you live your life. Your values shape your life and help define who you are. Your actions reflect those values.

Jack's Story

Values? I always thought I had great values. Of all the values, honor was something I took the most seriously. To me, honor meant never ever, under no circumstance, could I rat on a friend. It just wasn't done. And where did this value get me? Locked up. Where's my "friend"? Long gone. Never heard from him again once I landed here. This is where honor got me—in this cell.

Before entering this treatment program, I never thought about how I dishonored my mom, dad, and kids while committing crimes. Never once thought of it. All I thought of was that honor code with the drinking, drugging boys I hung out with. Nothin' else mattered.

— Jack S.,
serving time for dealing drugs and aggravated robbery

Traditional Values

Notice how the following traditional values have responsibility built into them:

SECURITY	I feel secure when I am reasonably sure about the future for my family and me.
INFLUENCE	I enjoy having my opinion respected by the people who are important to me. I like it when other people occasionally take my advice.
RECOGNITION	I like it when people notice who I am, especially when I have worked hard and have done a good job.
HELPFULNESS	I enjoy helping others, especially friends and family members, when they need or want my help.
FREEDOM	I want to be free to do as I wish, as long as I'm sure I'm not harming other people.
FRIENDLINESS	I care about other people. I'm willing to do what it takes to be a trustworthy friend.
SPIRITUALITY	I want to do what is right according to my spiritual beliefs. I value and respect other people's beliefs.
NEW EXPERIENCES	I enjoy doing new and different things, if I know that I won't harm other people by doing them.
FAMILY	I value and respect the people in my family.
ORDERLINESS	I like to be organized, but I respect that other people do things differently than I.

WEALTH	I like to have nice things, as long as I don't value things more than I value other people.
QUALITY	I want to do things well, but I know that I am not judged by what I do. Rather, I am judged by who I am.

Criminal Values

Notice how the following criminal values have self-centeredness built into them:

SECURITY	I am never satisfied or secure because I can't trust anyone but myself. I always want more of everything.
INFLUENCE	People must always respect me and do what I say. If they don't, I have the right to make them do what I want.
RECOGNITION	I should be noticed and praised for every effort. If I am criticized, I give myself permission to attack people.
HELPFULNESS	I like to help people because then they owe me. I do things even when they ask me not to because I'm the only one who can do it right.
FREEDOM	I want what I want, when I want it. I should be able to do whatever I want to do, no matter who it hurts.
FRIENDLINESS	I can have friends, if it suits me. I can act friendly, if it suits me. But no one should get too close to me.
SPIRITUALITY	I can act spiritual if it's part of the con. Other people's spiritual beliefs are stupid and wrong.

NEW EXPERIENCES	I get bored easily and expect to be entertained. I get to do whatever I want, as long as it's fun for me. I don't care who it hurts.
FAMILY	I say I love my family. But I'm willing to hurt them by getting high, lying, and being incarcerated. I'm willing to steal from them when I'm on the street. I beg them for money when I'm locked up. I make promises to change but never do.
ORDERLINESS	There's only one way—my way. Laws are made to be broken.
WEALTH	I deserve everything I can get, and I don't care who I have to hurt to get what I want.
QUALITY	I work as hard as I need to. No one can tell me anything. They are lucky to have me. If you criticize my job, you are disrespecting me.
USING	I get to use alcohol and other drugs. I get to use and abuse people, including family. Nothing matters to me more than alcohol or other drugs. This always comes first no matter what. I'm not happy unless I'm high.
POWER	No one has the right to tell me what to do. If someone tries, I get to do whatever it takes to get my power back. I need to be in control. I hate when others have power over me.

With criminal values, you are only concerned about how things affect you.

Now that you've learned about both traditional values and criminal values, it's time to look at yourself. What traditional and criminal values do you relate to most?

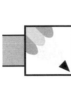

Looking at Your Traditional and Criminal Values

➤ Circle one traditional value that you identify with most.

security	recognition	freedom
influence	helpfulness	friendliness
spirituality	family	wealth
new experiences	orderliness	quality

➤ What do you value most about this traditional value? Why?

_____

_____

➤ Circle one criminal value that you identify with most.

security	recognition	freedom
influence	helpfulness	friendliness
spirituality	family	wealth
new experiences	orderliness	quality
using	power	

➤ What do you value most about this criminal value? Why?

_____

_____

You may feel like you're riding the fence here. On one hand, you want to do right by your family. You believe in the traditional values. But if you also believe you need to live by criminal values, then you feel conflicted. That's when win-lose values come into play.

Win-Lose Values

Our culture makes us think that conflicts call for a different set of values. We think the "good" values don't apply to **conflict.** Instead, we switch to using values designed for winning. We deceive, fight, put others down, treat others badly to "put them in their place," and see others as enemies and hate them. We want to win at all costs and by any means. Relationships suddenly turn nasty. You become a different person, and you're not happy. No one is happy.

> **Conflict**
>
> A struggle, clash, or fight is a *conflict.*

Jim's Story

Okay you guys, listen up! If you're anything like me, I'm sure it ticked you off plenty to read all that stuff about criminal values. It ticked me off the first time I saw it, too. See, I always thought of myself as a straight-up guy, convict code all the way. I figured they got no right to say I wasn't looking out for my family first.

My counselor had to tell me to take a breath, I was talking so fast. Then he asked me a simple question: "If you love your family more than anything, why did you keep doing the very things that would take you away from them?"

I tried to talk my way around it. I told him I was dealing drugs for my family. He said that I was full of it. I told him I had to deal 'cause it was the only way to get money for them. He said that was a crock. He said I was only fooling myself. I tried every way I know—but the truth is my number-one value on the street was getting high.

— Jim R.,
serving time for dealing drugs and manslaughter

If you've had a lot of conflict in your life, chances are you can relate to win-lose values. You know the values that make you feel good about yourself and build good relationships with others. But you think you can't live those values if you're going to win and get what you want in life. You might think it's a world of sharks, and shark values tell you to kill or be killed, to do it to others before they do it to you.

Win-lose values create a world full of conflict. It's that simple. And certainly many people act from such values—both behind bars and on the outside. Much of the world is nasty and dangerous as a result. Do you want to go back to society? Win-lose values have brought you where you are now. All they can ever give you, whether you're here or on the street, is more conflict.

In choosing your values, the bottom-line questions are

- Who do you want to be?
- How do you want to live?

The trick about values is sticking with them. Choosing traditional values doesn't help if you don't use them when you face difficult decisions and tough situations.

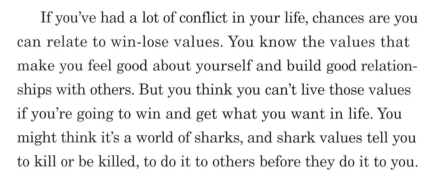

What kind of values do you want to have?

If you choose traditional values, conflict is not a time to let them go. That is when you need your values the most. Conflict tests your values by asking two questions: "What are your real values?" and "Who is the real you?" Conflict is a chance to find out what you're all about. Can you stand in the middle of a conflict and still live your values? Winning at all costs destroys marriages, families, businesses, and lifelong friendships. Win-lose values destroy lives. You need to try something else.

To get out of this mess, you need traditional, honest values that will work for you. What does it mean to bring the values of respect, honesty, courage, or even love to a conflict? You may not "win" in win-lose terms. But if you live your good values, you cannot lose. This is because you'll always have self-respect. Your life will be shaped by values you believe in and want to experience for yourself.

Values aren't just for the short term.

They build up your character, identity, and self-worth in the long term. Values are your foundation for living. Daily conflicts can either destroy you or improve you. You can either use them to keep conflict going, or practice healthy values to find out who you really are.

Jack's Story

Man! That really messed me up when they said I should be able to see my values in action while I was still in the joint. What a crock! Anyway, I've always said that I rate respect as one of my highest values. Truth be told, I was really only talking about other people respecting ME. But I know I need to show it to get it. So anyways, I tried to show a little respect to other people, even just in my head. Like I said, it messed me up, but I gotta admit I felt a little better about myself when I wasn't slamming other people so much.

— Jack S.,
serving time for dealing drugs and aggravated robbery

Defining Your Values

➤ Following is a list of values in alphabetical order. Rate how important they are to you in your life today. You can do this by placing an **H** next to the ones that have the highest importance for you, an **M** next to the ones of medium importance, and an **L** next to the ones of lowest importance. Remember, there are no right or wrong answers. Everyone has a different way of seeing things. For example, a peer may rate creativity as his highest value, while you may rate it as your lowest value. You're both right!

____ **Achievement**—I feel like I have accomplished something in work, school, or community.

____ **Creativity**—I express myself through art, music, writing, ideas, and so on.

____ **Family**—I am very involved in family life with my partner and/or children.

____ **Freedom**—I have the freedom to choose to do the things I want to do.

____ **Friendship**—I have close, mutually supportive relationships with others.

____ **Health**—I am physically, mentally, and emotionally well.

____ **Helpfulness and Service**—I do good in the world by helping others.

____ **Influence and Power**—I dominate and influence others, and I can make and enforce the rules.

____ **Orderliness**—I keep things neat, orderly, and organized.

____ **Respect**—I am admired by others and people think well of me.

____ **Security**—I have an idea of what the future holds for myself and my family.

____ **Sobriety**—I stay chemical free each day (one day at a time).

____ **Spirituality**—I believe in and have a close relationship with nature, humanity, a higher power, a deity, or a spirit of life.

____ **Variety**—I have new and different experiences often.

____ **Wealth**—I have a lot of money and possessions, far more than I need to live comfortably.

____ **Work**—I work toward a better life by holding down a job that has meaning and provides me with a good income.

➤ List your three most important values.　　　List your three least important values.

1. _____　_____

2. _____　_____

3. _____　_____

If these values are really important to you, you should be able to see them in action over the next few days.

Values are your ideas about what is most important to you in your life—what you want to live by and live for. They are the silent forces behind many of your actions and decisions.

Exercise 13 will help you see what you truly value in your life at this time. Do the best you can with this exercise. This is a difficult one because you have to listen to another person tell you what he or she sees in you. But listen carefully—that person might be right!

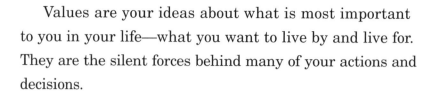

What Do You Value in Your Life?

Review your answers to exercise 12. Write each of your three most important values after the word *value* below. Answer the following questions for each of the values you list.

1. Value _____

    EXAMPLE:

    sobriety

    Your definition of this value:

    EXAMPLE:

    "I stay chemical free each day while taking it one day at a time."

_____

_____

_____

Give a real-life example of how you continue to struggle with this area:

EXAMPLE:

"I try to do it alone. I'm not working my recovery program."

_____

_____

_____

What do you need to do to improve this area of your life?

EXAMPLE:

"I need to start working my Twelve Step recovery program and stay chemical and crime free."

_____

_____

_____

_____

_____

_____

➤ 2. Value _____

Your definition of this value:

_____

_____

_____

Give a real-life example of how you continue to struggle with this area:

_____

_____

_____

_____

What do you need to do to improve this area of your life?

_____

_____

_____

_____

➤ 3. Value _____

   Your definition of this value:

   _____

   _____

   _____

   Give a real-life example of how you continue to struggle
   with this area:

   _____

   _____

   _____

   _____

   What do you need to do to improve this area of your life?

   _____

   _____

   _____

   _____

➤ Now, go over these questions with your peer. That person
   will then complete exercise 14, giving you insight and
   feedback on the values you have chosen.

Peer Evaluation

This exercise is to be completed by the person identified as the peer in exercise 13. There are a few important rules regarding feedback. First, always use "I" statements, such as "I think . . ." instead of "you" statements. Second, always ask yourself whether the information you're providing is helpful or hurtful. This is not the time to take a cheap shot at someone you have a grudge against.

➤ Your name (peer):

_____

You have been asked to review material on values of a peer who trusts you. The idea here is to provide constructive feedback to the person in order to help him recognize his strengths and his areas that need work.

➤ What areas do you see as strengths for this person?

EXAMPLE:

"He always has his assignments done on time."

_____

_____

_____

_____

_____

_____

➤ What areas do you see as needing work?

EXAMPLE:

"He jokes around too much during lecture."

_____

_____

_____

_____

_____

➤ What do you think keeps him from being the man he wants to be?

EXAMPLE:

"He needs to get serious about treatment."

_____

_____

_____

_____

_____

Values are your ideas about what is most important to you in your life— what you want to live by and live for.

Exercises 12, 13, and 14 have helped you learn a lot about your values. You've been able to see which values work and which don't work.

Relationships

Relationships have a lot to do with values. In this section, we'll evaluate the relationships you already have. You'll practice skills to look at each new relationship.

Healthy Problem-Solving in Relationships

Face it, relationships take a lot of work. It's time for a reality check. Real life is not some kind of fairy tale where you meet the person you always dreamed about and he or she is absolutely perfect. You'll never find this. After all, we're all human.

We make mistakes. We have our own ideas about how to do things. We might not always agree.

Realizing this, do you still want to form a healthy relationship with another person? If so, you'll need to learn a little about working through your problems.

First, let's do an exercise that looks at a time when you were in a relationship with someone and things didn't work out.

EXERCISE **15** EXERCISE

Relationship Troubles

➤ Think of someone you lost from your life because of an argument. Write that person's name here and his or her relationship to you, such as friend, family member, girlfriend, boyfriend, child, etc.

_____

_____

➤ What was the argument about?

_____

_____

➤ What happened after the argument ended?

_____

_____

➤ Who do you think was right? Why?

_____

_____

➤ Who do you think was wrong? Why?

_____

_____

➤ Was the fight worth losing the relationship? (check one)

_____ Yes   _____ No

Why?

_____

_____

If you want healthy relationships, you are going to need to work on them. Exercise 16 gives some tips for effective problem solving, especially in relationships.

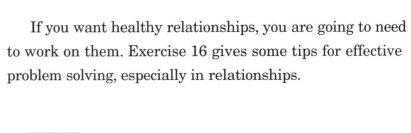

Solving Problems in Your Relationships

Five ways to solve problems with your relationships are given below. Read each one. Then, list an example from your own life when you solved a problem using each method.

➤ 1. **Compromise.** Nobody is always right or always wrong. Compromise means being flexible with someone else.

> EXAMPLE:
>
> *John wanted to go to the movies and Mary wanted to see her family. They compromised and went to an early movie, then to her parents' house.*

When have you compromised to solve a problem?

_____

_____

_____

_____

_____

➤ 2. **Do not attack.** You do not bring up issues and problems that neither of you can change. You can't undo something that you've done in the past, but you can deal with your emotions that result from those past behaviors.

> EXAMPLE:
>
> *Juan and Sam had been in rival gangs. In the treatment program, they agreed to put the past behind them.*

When have you made the decision to not attack in order to solve a problem?

_____

_____

_____

_____

_____

➤ 3. **Focus on the now.** Stick to the issue you are arguing about. Agree on what issue will be discussed and focus on that. Don't bring up old issues.

> EXAMPLE:
>
> *Dan's celly woke him up too early when Dan first moved in. They worked that out. When Dan wanted his celly to turn down his radio, Dan didn't remind him of their previous argument. Dan just told him to turn the music down.*

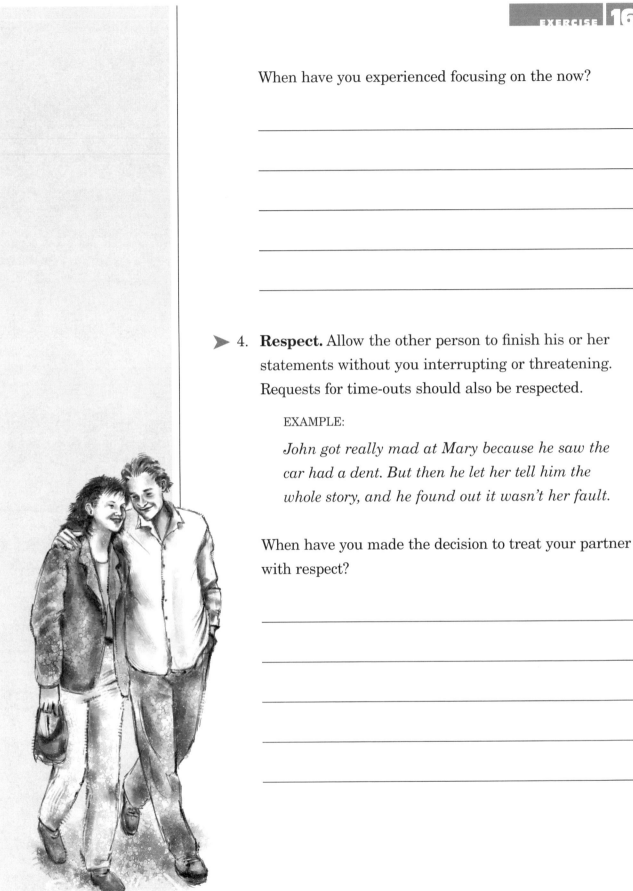

When have you experienced focusing on the now?

_____

_____

_____

_____

_____

➤ 4. **Respect.** Allow the other person to finish his or her statements without you interrupting or threatening. Requests for time-outs should also be respected.

   EXAMPLE:

   John got really mad at Mary because he saw the car had a dent. But then he let her tell him the whole story, and he found out it wasn't her fault.

When have you made the decision to treat your partner with respect?

_____

_____

_____

_____

➤ 5. **Use "I" statements.** Avoid "you," "us," or "we" when referring to the issue. Taking responsibility will make the other person feel less defensive. Using "I" statements is a good way of giving feedback to someone else. The "I" statement does not blame or judge the other person. To practice this, change the "you" statements listed below to "I" statements. You might want to use "I feel" or "I want" or "I'm upset." The first statement is already changed to give you an example.

"You" Statements	"I" Statements
• You never listen.	• I feel like you didn't listen to what I said.
• You always ignore me.	
• You think you are better than me.	
• You always interrupt me.	
• You never let me do anything.	
• You don't understand me.	
• You need to grow up and stop acting like a baby.	

Getting Along with Your Family

Before you start this section, go back to exercise 3, Exploring Your Family History, on page 21. Have any of your answers changed since you've been in treatment? Do you see some of your family members differently now? Remember, family work is not looking for heroes and villains. It's just taking a look at where you came from and asking yourself where you want to go.

It's also important to know what healthy and unhealthy families look like. Knowing this will help you to take the steps you need for the type of family you want.

Unhealthy families have rules like

- Don't talk; keep secrets
- Don't feel; don't express feelings; stuff feelings
- Don't trust; don't expect accountability
- Deny; blame others; never accept responsibility
- Pretend everything is okay; play it safe
- Don't make waves

What works in families?

- Caring about each other
- Showing support for other family members
- Defining boundaries
- Honoring the good things

What doesn't work in families?

- Helping family members with criminal activity
- Seeking revenge
- Letting family members define who you are
- Ignoring the painful stuff

Many incarcerated men are the ***scapegoats*** in their families—the bad boys who always get in trouble and who are blamed for the behavior of others. In healthy families, the past does not dictate the future. That means, if you were the scapegoat in the past, you don't have to be one in the future.

EXERCISE 17 EXERCISE

The Payoffs of Being a Scapegoat

If you were the family scapegoat in the past, what were some of your payoffs? For example, scapegoats can be scary guys. Did you scare people, and as a result, did you have a lot of power in your family? Write down as many payoffs as you can. If you were not a scapegoat in your family, think of other groups of people that treated you like a scapegoat. It could be your neighbors who blamed you for all the bad things that happened there.

> **Scapegoat**
>
> A *scapegoat* is a person (or group) who is blamed for the behavior of others. A scapegoat is an easy target.

➤ **My Payoffs**

1. _____

    _____

2. _____

    _____

3. _____

    _____

4. _____

    _____

Your family had payoffs, too. For example, *all* of the family problems can be blamed on the scapegoat. Did you get blamed for things that had nothing to do with you? Write as many payoffs for your family as you can. Once again, if you weren't the family scapegoat, write down the payoffs for the group you identified on the previous page.

➤ **My Family's Payoffs**

1. _____

_____

2. _____

_____

3. _____

_____

4. _____

_____

What could you gain from giving up the scapegoat role? What could your family gain? In part 3, we'll look at how to break out of these cycles.

Family Violence

Parents do not usually make conscious decisions to abuse their children. It happens for a variety of reasons. They may be emotionally immature or unable to understand their child's behavior at certain stages. Maybe they don't have a clue how to raise a child. Genetics might play a part in this, too. Depression, other mental illnesses, and alcohol and other drug abuse may contribute to family violence. Keep in mind that while people are using alcohol and other drugs, violence is more likely to happen. When people aren't using, they may be the best parents—but when they start using, things change.

The roots of family violence are not surprising. Many abusive parents were abused themselves as children. Violence is a learned pattern of behavior stemming from early childhood experiences.

Parenting

Author Gary Smalley has identified four basic parenting styles. These styles will help you identify whether you have healthy or unhealthy parenting styles.

1. ***Dominating.*** An overly dominant parent has a lot of laws and is very rigid. This parent has a high amount of control and exhibits very little warmth or affection.

2. ***Neglectful.*** This type of parent has very few rules and shows very little love. This parent often fails to give loving support and is perceived as uncaring. These parents generally show little interest in their children's day-to-day lives.

3. ***Permissive.*** This parent is extremely loving but has very few rules. This parent gives the children warmth, support, and unconditional love, but is inconsistent and nonassertive with rules and limits.

4. **Balanced.** This type of parent has clearly defined rules with an equal amount of love. The parent is very affectionate and supportive but displays control. This parenting style results in willingness to obey rules and authority.

Parenting Style

You have looked at four parenting styles: dominating, neglectful, permissive, and balanced. All of these will be used in this exercise.

➤ Which parenting style is closest to the way you were raised, and why?

> EXAMPLE:
>
> *"I was raised in a dominating style. My dad ruled the roost. His word was law. I was scared of him, and I avoided him."*

_____

_____

_____

_____

➤ Which style is closest to the way you act today?

> EXAMPLE:
>
> *"I'm permissive. I don't want my kids to go through what I did. My wife says I let them get away with murder."*

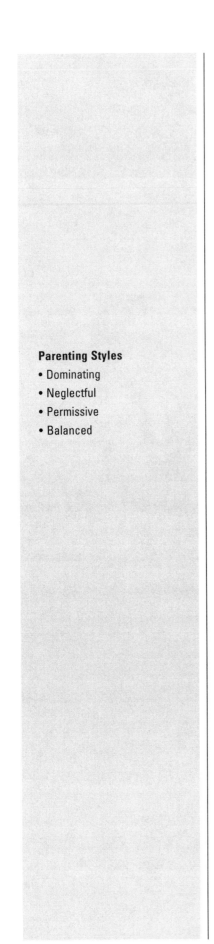

Parenting Styles
• Dominating
• Neglectful
• Permissive
• Balanced

_____

_____

_____

_____

➤ What do you need to do to be more balanced?

EXAMPLE:

*"I need to use the same rules as their mom.
I need to be the heavy sometimes, too."*

_____

_____

_____

_____

Healthy Belonging

We all need other people. There are very few hermits either inside or outside of incarceration. We might not like to admit it, but we don't know everything. We can't do everything on our own. We need to love and be loved. We need to be respected in our relationships. In order for all of this to happen, we need to take some risks in relationships and learn how to be healthier. We need to learn that each person is important—this includes the kids, the annoying neighbor, and even the PO.

Coping is dealing
with problems without
losing your temper.

Chances are, how you ***coped,*** or dealt, with something
in the past might not work for you today. Recognizing this
is very important. By doing so, you have begun your journey
on the road to recovery and change. Some things work out
well in the short term, but not in the long term.

 EXERCISE **19** EXERCISE

The Quick Fix

Think back to your past (include the recent past, here
in treatment). Ask yourself when you've used a quick fix,
or short-term solution, that later jammed you up.

Quick Fixes

➤ List four quick fixes you have used in the past.

EXAMPLE:

*"I didn't like the way the guy was talking to me
so I punched him in the nose."*

1. _____

_____

Jim's Story

What works and what doesn't work in my life today? Lots of things.
What worked when I was growing up doesn't work so well now. I was in
survival mode, man. Just trying to make it alone. I didn't need nothing
from nobody. That's how I coped. It was a dog-eat-dog world and I was
the king mutt.

— Jim R.,
serving time for dealing drugs and manslaughter

2. _____

_____

3. _____

_____

4. _____

_____

➤ Problems That Quick Fixes Have Caused

EXAMPLE:

"I was still on paper and I got revoked for smacking him."

1. _____

_____

2. _____

_____

3. _____

_____

4. _____

_____

How you coped, or dealt, with something in the past might not work for you today.

➤ **Long-Term Solutions to the Problem**

EXAMPLE:

*"All I had to do was walk away from the guy
and I wouldn't be sitting here now."*

1.  _____

_____

2.  _____

_____

3. _____

_____

4. 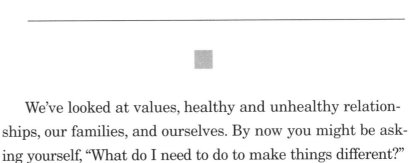 _____

_____

**What do you need
to do to make
things different?**

We've looked at values, healthy and unhealthy relationships, our families, and ourselves. By now you might be asking yourself, "What do I need to do to make things different?"

To answer that question, you need to do a personal
inventory. You may ask, "What's that?" Did you ever work a
job where you had to take a physical inventory? This might
be counting all the merchandise in a store or warehouse. If
you haven't done this yourself, probably some of the people
around you have. The main thing about an inventory is that
it covers everything that's there. The same thing is true for
a personal inventory. Taking your personal inventory will
help you see what you need to do to make things different.

Doing a Personal Inventory

In order to see what needs to change in your life and what doesn't, we'll make a few lists. Under each category, write down two things you can't change. Then write down how you can deal with each thing in a positive way. We've provided a few examples in each category to get you started.

Genetics

EXAMPLES:

Things I CAN'T Change	Things I CAN Change
1. I am bald.	1. How I deal with losing my hair.
2. I have diabetes.	2. How I take care of my disease.

➤ Write down two examples of things that you were born into or with.

Things I CAN'T Change

Things I CAN Change

1. _____

   _____

2. _____

   _____

1. _____

   _____

2. _____

   _____

Taking your personal inventory will help you see what you need to do to make things different.

Family

EXAMPLE:

Things I CAN'T Change	Things I CAN Change
What family I was born into.	How I deal with my family today.

➤ Write down two examples that involve your family.

Things I CAN'T Change	Things I CAN Change
1. _____	1. _____
_____	_____
2. _____	2. _____
_____	_____

Early Chemical Use and Its Effects

EXAMPLE:

Things I CAN'T Change	Things I CAN Change
I dropped out of school in the ninth grade.	How I get an education while incarcerated.

➤ Write down two examples that involve you.

Things I CAN'T Change	Things I CAN Change
1. _____	1. _____
_____	_____
2. _____	2. _____
_____	_____

Boundaries

EXAMPLE:

Things I CAN'T Change	Things I CAN Change
I was sexually abused as a child.	How I treat children.

➤ Write down two examples that involve your boundaries.

Things I CAN'T Change	Things I CAN Change
1. _____ _____	1. _____ _____
2. _____ _____	2. _____ _____

Intimacy

EXAMPLE:

Things I CAN'T Change	Things I CAN Change
I was never loved as a child.	How I raise my kids.

➤ Write down two examples that involve intimacy.

Things I CAN'T Change	Things I CAN Change
1. _____ _____	1. _____ _____
2. _____ _____	2. _____ _____

Shame

EXAMPLE:

Things I CAN'T Change	Things I CAN Change
My past actions have let people down.	How I act now.

➤ Write down two examples that involve shame.

Things I CAN'T Change	Things I CAN Change
1. _____ _____	1. _____ _____
2. _____ _____	2. _____ _____

Culture

EXAMPLE:

Things I CAN'T Change	Things I CAN Change
People in my culture drink wine at every meal.	How I respond when wine is offered to me.

➤ Write down two examples that involve your culture.

Things I CAN'T Change	Things I CAN Change
1. _____ _____	1. _____ _____
2. _____ _____	2. _____ _____

Jim's Story

Man, I hated doing that inventory. I hate looking at stuff in black-and-white that makes me look like a chump. I've done some messed-up shit in my life. I love my family, but nobody taught them how to take care of kids. Sometimes I felt so screwed up that I didn't think there's any reason to try to change. But if you feel that way, I tell you, it gets better. I took an honest look at who I am and it wasn't pretty, but it was me all right!

— Jim R.,
serving time for dealing drugs and manslaughter

Medicating the Pain

You may have thought alcohol or other drugs would help you cope with life. You probably got high because *at first* it seemed to work. Maybe, your mom and dad were fighting every night, getting high was a way to tune it all out. Maybe you went out with friends every night so you could forget about what was happening at home. But eventually, medicating your pain by getting high doesn't work as well.

Medicating Your Problems with Alcohol or Other Drugs

Under the heading "It Worked," identify four situations when you got high and it seemed to work, at least for the short term. Under the heading "It Didn't Work," identify situations when it didn't work out so well, at least in the long term.

➤ **It Worked**

EXAMPLE:

"I was too shy to ask a girl to dance. After a couple of drinks, I went right up to her."

1. _____

   _____

2. _____

   _____

3. _____

   _____

4. _____

   _____

➤ **It Didn't Work**

EXAMPLE:

*"I was scared because I lost my job. I got high
and tried to rob the place."*

1. _____

_____

2. _____

_____

3. _____

_____

4. _____

_____

Anger

Anger is one feeling that you've probably tried to deal with
by getting high. Anger usually comes from fear, frustration,
or hurt. It's the "knotting up inside."

Anger is an emotion that tells us something is wrong.

Everyone gets angry sometimes, but some of us use our
anger as a way to control others. Look at exercise 22 for
a list of payoffs from getting and staying angry.

Payoffs from My Anger

➤ Place an **X** next to the payoffs that sound like your behavior when you're angry.

_____ I can blame other people for my situation or feelings.

_____ I get what I want because people are afraid of me.

_____ I get attention and it makes me feel important and powerful.

_____ I put up a "wall" because I'm afraid of getting close to others.

_____ I can manipulate others with guilt. That way they will look at their behavior, and I don't have to look at mine.

_____ I can use anger to avoid looking bad. Then, I don't have to be threatened by others' feelings.

_____ I can feel sorry for myself and say to myself, "No one understands me."

_____ I don't have to slow down and think about my feelings.

Look at the payoffs you selected. Can you think of healthier ways to feel good about yourself? For example, if you chose "I can blame other people for my situation or feelings," it's probably because your choices keep getting you jammed up. If you made better choices, you wouldn't have to blow up all the time.

➤ On the next page, list three of the payoffs you selected. Then, write about a healthier way to deal with each problem.

1. _____

   _____

   _____

2. _____

   _____

   _____

3. _____

   _____

   _____

Mindlessly venting anger at another person will not solve problems.

Long-Term Solutions for Anger

Mindlessly venting anger at another person will not solve problems. Instead, it will add to the original problems. The same can be said for running away from anger or pretending that you're never angry.

When we express our anger appropriately, we are being honest, which makes for a better relationship. We can learn how to trust others enough to be our real self with them.

Many times anger works like an umbrella to protect us from the cold rain of uncomfortable emotions. For example, it's easier to blow up at your boss when you're late for work than feel the shame of not taking care of yourself. Some of the feelings that anger "protects" us from include sadness, loneliness, confusion, and fear. We still feel these feelings, but by blowing up, we hide these feelings from other people.

The Umbrella of Anger

What feelings do you hide from others under your anger umbrella? Answer the following questions as honestly as you can. You might be surprised by the answers.

➤ Have you ever been sad and pretended that you were angry instead?

> EXAMPLE:
>
> *A guy breaks up with his girlfriend, goes to a bar, and gets in a fight. Is he really angry or does he think he'll look soft if people know he is sad?*

_____

_____

_____

_____

_____

➤ Have you ever been lonely and pretended that you were angry instead?

> EXAMPLE:
>
> *A guy who is locked up and not getting any visits at Christmas picks a fight with his celly. Is he really angry or does he not want to admit that he's lonely?*

_____

_____

_____

_____

_____

_____

➤ Have you ever been confused and pretended that you were
angry instead?

    EXAMPLE:

    A guy buys a fancy bike for his child's birthday.
    The night before, when he's trying to put it together,
    he can't figure out how to get the handlebars on.
    He gets in a big fight with his wife, storms out,
    and heads for the bar. Is he really angry or is he
    confused about how to do something?

_____

_____

_____

_____

_____

➤ Have you ever been afraid and pretended that you were angry instead?

EXAMPLE:

A guy does not want to meet his girl's parents because he thinks his criminal record will make them put him down. Instead of telling his girl that he's nervous, he tells her she can't go visit her parents. Is he really angry or is he afraid?

_____

_____

_____

_____

_____

Jack's Story

I hated having to admit that I was sad or lonely or confused or scared. Sometimes feelings are really a bitch. But being pissed off all the time just got me in here. Look at fear. It's like fear is the real "f" word around the joint. You always hear guys say they're not scared of anything. But that's crap. This ain't a nice place to call home. I guess if I have enough guts to admit I'm afraid sometimes, you probably do, too.

— Jack S.,
  serving time for dealing drugs and aggravated robbery

How Can I Do a Better Job on My Anger?

Working on handling your anger can be very rewarding, but you've got to have a plan. Two steps for handling your anger appropriately are

1. Ask yourself what about the situation makes you angry.

2. Look at the feelings *under* your anger. What it is that you are really angry about?

These are not easy steps. Asking yourself what makes you angry might seem like it would be simple to do. However, often we are really angry before we think about that question. Help lower your anger by slowing down, trying not to take yourself too seriously, and letting go of old grudges. In part 3, we'll look more deeply at ways to challenge how we deal with anger.

The next exercise is about self-hate and how it relates to our anger problems. Self-hatred is a combination of anger and shame turned inward. The anger makes people attack themselves whenever they do anything wrong or when they fail at something. The shame makes them think they will never get better. Together, anger and shame produce this thought: "I screwed up my life in the past, I'm screwing it up now, and I will certainly screw it up in the future."

It's difficult to treat others decently when you are being mean to yourself.

Self-Hate and Anger Management

➤ A checklist of some self-hating thoughts and actions are listed below. Place an **X** in front of the ones you can relate to.

_____ I get angry at myself a lot.

_____ I often neglect my own basic needs, such as making doctor appointments when I'm sick.

_____ I don't like the way I look, what I do, how I think, who I am.

_____ I often think "I'm no good," "I'm not good enough," "I'm unlovable," or "I don't belong."

_____ I call myself "stupid," "worthless," or "ugly."

_____ I swear at myself.

_____ I ignore praise or refuse to believe it when people say nice things about me.

_____ I often fail at what I do because I expect to fail or believe I don't deserve success.

_____ I think of myself as hopeless. I'll never be good at anything or for anyone.

➤ Total the number of items you could relate to in the list above. _____

If you placed an **X** next to two or more items, you may be full of self-hate. Regardless of how many items you checked with an **X**, try to give respect to others and yourself. Remember that self-hate may ruin your efforts to be healthier with your anger. If you don't start treating yourself better, you probably won't be able to keep control of your anger.

➤ What one item from the list will you continue to work on throughout this workbook? How will you go about doing this?

EXAMPLE:

If you decide not to swear at yourself, then don't swear at other people either.

_____

_____

_____

_____

_____

Exercise 25 is the most time-consuming in this workbook. This exercise will give you the chance to see patterns in your relationships. It will also help you decide whether your way of dealing with friends, family, and sexual partners is working—or whether you need to change the way you relate to others. This exercise will be useless to you if you are not honest.

Relationship History

The purpose of this exercise is to show you patterns in your relationships. It will also help you decide whether how you are dealing with people is actually working. After completing this exercise, you may decide that you want to change the way you relate to certain people. You must be honest for this exercise to work.

Read the information on pages 102–107 carefully before you complete the blank charts on pages 110–113. Note that each letter and number in the information refers to a square in the blank charts. To get you started, we've provided you with a sample chart on pages 108–109. Take a few minutes to look at the sample chart before beginning to complete the blank chart.

➤ **People with Whom I Have Relationships**

Choose a person for each number. Write that person's name underneath the corresponding number on the charts on pages 110–113. (See sample charts on pages 108–109 for examples.)

1. Primary female caregiver: mother, stepmother, foster mother, older sister, aunt, grandmother, father's girlfriend, etc.

2. Primary male caregiver: father, stepfather, foster father, older brother, uncle, grandfather, mother's boyfriend, etc.

3. First friend

4. First romantic relationship/crush—this may have included some touching

5. First sexual relationship—this may or may not have included sexual intercourse, but does include sexual touch

6. Second sexual relationship

7. Additional important relationship, including your last or most current sexual relationship

8. Additional important relationship (friendship or sexual relationship)

9. Additional important relationship (friendship or sexual relationship)

10. Additional important relationship (friendship or sexual relationship)

Descriptions

Answer the following questions for each person you chose. Write your answers in the corresponding boxes on pages 110–113. (See sample charts on pages 108–109 for examples.)

A. (Characteristics of person) Using the list of positive and negative attributes on page 106, describe the person as honestly as you can. For example, the person may have been loving at times and controlling at other times. No one is all good or all bad. Being honest will help you see patterns in your relationships It will also help you see what your responsibility was in the relationship you are describing. For each person, list three positive and three negative attributes.

B. (Characteristics of relationship) Using the list of healthy and unhealthy relationship characteristics on page 107, describe the relationship as honestly as you can. For example, you may have experienced the relationship as being safe at times and dangerous at other times List at least two positive and two negative characteristics for each relationship.

C. (How the relationship began) Be honest in describing how the relationship began. How did you meet the person? Describe any vulnerability you observed in your potential partner, such as physical or mental disability, addiction, etc. Describe what you hoped to gain by being in this relationship, such as money, power, sex, access to other victims, alcohol or other drugs, some kind of "get back" at a former partner, etc. Also, write down how long the relationship lasted.

D. (My role, my feelings) What did the person expect of you? For example, were you the caretaker, the victim, the dealer, the pimp, the paycheck, or some other role?

How genuine were you with your feelings? For example, did you lie and say "I love you" to get sexual favors? Did you pretend to care about a "friend" because he had a good supply of drugs? Were you able to admit when you were scared, confused, or sad? In the case of sexual relationships, were you faithful to your partner? Was your partner faithful to you?

E. (Rewards of the relationship) What did you receive from the relationship? For example, did you receive money, clothes, drugs, or a place to stay? Did the relationship provide a cover for you so that you could continue to lead a double life? Did you get an increase in self-esteem because you controlled someone else?

F. (Cost of the relationship) What did you have to "pay" to keep the relationship going? For example, did you have to hide parts of yourself from the other person? Were you used or degraded in the relationship? Did you believe you had to make the other person happy? Did the relationship damage your self-esteem? Were you cut off from family or friends?

G. (Chemical use in the relationship) What chemicals did you use during the course of the relationship? What chemicals did the other person use? Did either of you attempt sobriety? What impact did the use of chemicals have on the relationship, such as money spent or impact on sexuality?

H. (Ending the relationship) How did the relationship end? At the time, did you think that the end of the relationship was your responsibility? Do you see the end of the relationship differently now? In the case of sexual relationships, did you have another partner lined up before you ended the first relationship? Have you allowed yourself to grieve the loss of past relationships?

Positive Attributes

Beautiful	Honest	Positive
Confident	Humble	Powerful
Content	Humorous	Secure
Courageous	Intelligent	Sincere
Forgiving	Loving	Spiritual
Friendly	Optimistic	Strong
Generous	Passionate	Trustworthy
Gentle	Patient	Willing
Graceful	Peaceful	Wise

Negative Attributes

Aggressive	Harsh	Phony
Angry	Hateful	Rageful
Bitter	Hopeless	Resentful
Bored	Humorless	Rigid
Cold	Impatient	Rough
Cowardly	Insecure	Suspicious
Cruel	Listless	Unsympathetic
Dishonest	Miserly	Unthinking
Gossiping	Negative	Vengeful
Grandiose	Negligent	Weak
Greedy	Panicky	

Healthy Relationship Characteristics

Communication   Equality   Safety

Cooperation   Love   Tenderness

Dependability   Negotiation   Trust

Unhealthy Relationship Characteristics

Antagonism   Disloyalty   Ultimatums

Control   Hierarchy   Unloving

Danger   Manipulation   Violence

■   ■   ■

Check out what you've learned. Begin by looking for multiple uses of the same word. For example, if you described several of your partners as "suspicious," what does this tell you about your behavior? If you described them as "weak," how can you challenge your attraction to this type of person? Then look at the words you didn't choose. Are there some qualities from the positive attributes list that never occur in your description of past and current sexual partners? These may include attributes such as "strong" or "confident." Are these qualities you wish your partners had? Do you have these qualities yourself?

Because of what you have learned in this exercise, you may want to change the way you relate to certain people. That's okay. This exercise is designed for you to learn more about your relationships.

My Relationship History (Example)

	1. Doris, Foster Mom	2. Jim, Foster Dad	3. George	4. Mary	5. Sally
A	+ Honest + Humorous + Strong - Cold - Rough - Bitter	+ Trustworthy + Intelligent + Friendly - Weak - Miserly - Insecure	+ Honest + Humorous + Strong - Unthinking - Impatient - Aggressive	+ Peaceful + Graceful + Beautiful - Humorless - Phony - Gossiping	+ Loving + Passionate + Positive - Dishonest - Phony - Greedy
B	+ Trust + Safety + Dependability - Manipulation - Unloving - Hierarchy	+ Trust + Safety + Dependability - Violence - Danger - Control	+ Communication + Cooperative - Violence - Danger - Ultimatums	+ Tenderness + Trust + Love - Manipulation - Unloving - Hierarchy	+ Cooperation + Communication - Manipulation - Hierarchy - Antagonism
C	Picked me up from County at age 2. I trusted her, but she pretended to love me to get money. Treated her own kids better.	I was scared of him at first. He never hit me but he smashed things. He'd take me to the garage and show me cars.	We were 12. I liked him because he was funny and cool. He liked to do dangerous things. He liked to fight when he was drinking.	We met when I was 13. She was the first girl I kissed. Her family was more important than me. She said she loved me but she lied.	Sally went to George first. He dumped her, and I got her. We had sex and drank. She used me to get back at George. She wanted money.
D	She wanted me to say "I love you" and call her "mom." She used me to make herself look good. If I cried, she'd say, "I'll give you something to cry about."	He made money on me. I worked for him for many years and never got paid. He'd call me "son" in front of other people but not when alone.	I was the butt of a lot of jokes. I had to pretend my feelings weren't hurt or he'd never stick around. He beat me up when drunk.	She was my neighbor. She wanted to have a boyfriend, and I was handy. She dumped me for a football player.	She always wanted to kiss and neck in front of George. She wanted sex right away. She complained about money. I found out she was still sleeping with George.

My Relationship History (Example)

	1. Doris, Foster Mom	2. Jim, Foster Dad	3. George	4. Mary	5. Sally
E	She made me feel like I was in a real family at first, but she treated her own kids better than me. I got my own room ,but I was in the basement.	I think he loved me, but I'm not sure. He taught me how to fix cars and drink. He lied to Mom for me. I felt good when he called me "son" and hugged me.	I felt cool hanging around him. Other people were scared of him and they got scared of me, too. Girls started to talk to me when I was with him.	I felt like a tough guy around her. She was beautiful so I thought everybody was jealous. We kissed and necked.	I was attracted to her when she was with George. She cried on my shoulder. I felt strong. We had sex the first night. I was glad to make George jealous.
F	I couldn't let her see my tears. I had to pretend I didn't notice she treated her kids better. I wanted to be in a good family so I pretended I was.	He sexually abused me when I was 10. He made me drink with him. He told me the abuse was my fault. He made me swear on the Bible not to tell.	He made me feel stupid because he knew more than me. He used me for an alibi. He was a lot stronger than me and called me a wimp.	I had to pretend to like her friend or she'd pout. I had to give her presents and compliment her all the time. I felt bad when she left.	She embarrassed me and told people I was a virgin. She made me ashamed that we were poor. When I found out she was with George, she laughed at me.
G	She was sober. I started drinking when I was 10. My foster dad hid it from her.	He was a binge drinker. He'd drink when my foster mom was away from home.	I turned him on to alcohol when we were 12. We'd steal it from my foster dad. We started pot at 15.	She didn't use at all.	She smoked pot and drank. She blamed the pot on sleeping with George.
H	In my first treatment, I told about my foster dad abusing me. She called me a liar and threw me out.	I left home at 15 when he let her kick me out. He called me one time and said he was sorry, but he was drunk.	I didn't want to see him after he got Sally back.	She dumped me for a football player.	She went back to George, and I went into treatment.

	1.	2.	3.	4.	5.
A					
B					
C					
D					

My Relationship History

	1.	2.	3.	4.	5.
E					
F					
G					
H					

	6.	7.	8.	9.	10.
A					
B					
C					
D					

	6.	7.	8.	9.	10.
E					
F					
G					
H					

Throughout part 2, you've taken an in-depth look at what works and what doesn't work. Now, it's time to look at what needs to change if you are going to be successful at living a life you can be proud of—one that doesn't put you behind bars.

"You might love your family dearly, you might plan to spend some time with them, but that doesn't mean you always want 'em as part of your support system. You've got to be honest with yourself about that."

— Roland V., former offender, Wisconsin

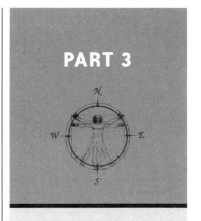

How Do
I Change?

Congratulations! You've already started to lay
the foundation for change by getting this far in the
workbook. By now, you've figured out a lot about
what works and what doesn't work in your life.
You know it's not really about what happened to
you in the past. It's about how you handle what
happened.

How you think, feel, and handle things today has a lot to do with your past. Our skills, attitudes, and values play a big part in our lives. It's time to look at *how* people change.

If you want to change, there are a few things you need to do. This involves

- knowing yourself
- taking care of yourself
- valuing yourself
- figuring out where you are

Knowing Yourself

If you want to make changes in your life, you need to take the time to know more about yourself. You can do that by asking yourself these questions:

- Are you doing a good job of taking care of your life?
- If someone else treated you the way you treat yourself, would you put up with it?

To really know yourself, you need to know the difference between what you want and what you need.

Taking Care of Yourself

Start with the basics and go from there. Without our basic needs being met, it is impossible to work on other issues. Right now, you're incarcerated and your basic needs are being met—you've got food, water, and shelter.

A psychologist named Abraham Maslow studied people's needs and came up with a hierarchy of needs. He designed a pyramid that shows what you need in order to become the man you want to be. Take a look at the pyramid on page 117.

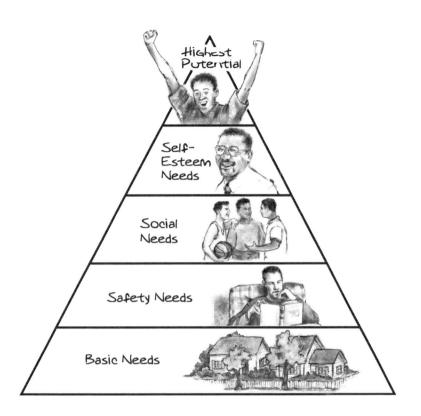

There are five levels of needs. The bottom layer is our most *basic needs*—food, water, and shelter. The second layer shows *safety needs*. This is feeling reasonably safe. The third layer is *social needs*. This is the feeling of belonging, being accepted, and having friends who care about you. The fourth layer is *self-esteem needs*. This deals with self-worth. And the last layer or the highest peak of the pyramid is *highest potential*. This is being your highest self—the man you want to be. This may be the same man you have pretended to be.

Valuing Yourself

Everybody wants to see themselves at the top of the heap. But sometimes how we try to get there backfires on us. Have you tried to meet your needs for self-esteem by controlling others? That's like frying an egg in the toaster! It seems like it would work. You have a source of heat that is sufficient to fry the egg. The problem is it makes a mess and ruins both the egg and the toaster.

When you try to feel better about yourself by putting someone else down, it seems like it will work—just like the egg in the toaster. But if you don't have good self-esteem, hurting other people won't give it to you. Real self-esteem comes from doing the right thing even when it's painful. Below is a list of five steps for change. Take your time as you read through these. They might look simple, but they are not easy.

Five Steps to Changing the Pain of the Past into Possibilities for the Future

Step 1 — Things that don't kill us, make us stronger. Even though your past may have been painful, you're still here. You got through it somehow. So, you can probably get through whatever you are struggling with now.

Step 2— Watch your thinking! When something painful happens to you, do you say things to yourself like "This is the worst thing that has ever happened to me. I will never be the same. I am a failure"? If you talk to yourself like that, you'll convince yourself that you are right. If you say to yourself "This is tough, but I can get through it!" that will be true, too.

Step 3— Avoid the blame game. Painful things are not always someone's fault. If we have self-hatred, we blame ourselves for things that have nothing to do with us. Or we might blame others for things they have no control over. Instead of blaming other people, just say to yourself "What can I do about it now?"

Step 4— Feel your feelings. When painful things happen to us, we feel pain. If you deny that there is pain, you are more likely to pretend to be angry. Is that one of the things that got you where you are today? Even if you can't admit it to anyone else, admit it to yourself when you've been hurt. It gives you a better chance of moving on.

Step 5— Practice. Try to remember times in the past when something that was painful turned out for the best. For example, lots of guys are secretly grateful that they got locked up because they know they couldn't have stopped using on their own. Practice taking the pain of the past and turning it into possibilities for the future.

Figuring Out Where You Are

How can you figure out where you are on the road to your highest potential? You need to learn how to find out where you are on your life's map. After all, you are the expert on you. The first thing to do is to take an honest look at whether or not you are really ready to make changes.

Maybe you are. Maybe you are not. Maybe you think it's *life* that needs to change, not you. Maybe you think your run of bad luck is over, and when you get out, you'll be able to do the same things you used to do, but without consequences. Maybe you think about giving up the criminal lifestyle. Maybe you think about quitting every New Year's Eve or some other time of the year. But then you convince yourself that you don't need to change after all. Or maybe you see that your problem is *you*. This is the beginning of real change.

It's okay if you are not totally gung ho every single second of the day. The point is that you realize that you've got problems and *you* need to change to get rid of them. Take a look at the list below. These are the six main stages in the change process.

Six Stages of Change

Stage 1 — Pre-awareness: Before you're even thinking about changing. At this stage, you're not thinking about changing anything. It's not that you can't see the solution. It's that you don't even see the problem!

Stage 2 — Contemplation: Thinking about changing. Here you have an idea that something is wrong in your life. You kind of see the problem, and you begin to think about what to do.

Stage 3 — Preparation: Getting ready to change. You see the problem and you are planning to take action. You want to change and you feel ready to change. But you still have mixed feelings about doing this.

Stage 4 — Taking action. You begin to change your behaviors. You do something—stop smoking, stop drinking, stop using. You take action.

Stage 5 — Avoiding relapse. You don't slip back into negative thinking or behaviors.

Stage 6 — Maintenance. Change doesn't end with the action stage. You have to stay changed. You work to make the change stick. You struggle to prevent relapse.

**Remember,
change will feel uncomfortable.**

Values and Change

Review the six stages of change on the previous page. What stage do you think you are at? Ideally, you should be at stage 3. This is when you see the problem and you are planning to take action. Values will help you get ready to make these changes in your life.

Values were discussed in part 2. As you know, people's values are their beliefs and ideas about what is really important in life. Our attitudes and behavior often reflect these beliefs and ideas. You learned that it's not about getting ahead in the *short term*. It's about building up your character, identity, and self-worth in the *long term*. Life brings daily conflicts and challenges. These can either destroy you or build you up. Don't let them destroy you. Instead, practice healthy values. This will build character and self-worth.

Jim's Story

When I got in the program and looked at the six stages of change, I figured they wanted me to be in stage 3, so that's how I talked. I told the counselor that I wanted to change, but I was still planning on getting high when I got out. I figured I could get away with it once. 'Course every time I get out I say that I'm only gonna use once, or only booze, or only on the weekend, and it never works. Right now, I really am in stage 3, I really want to change, and really have a lot of those "mixed feelings." It's easy to stay straight on the inside. I'm trying to tell the truth now. So I let people know when I feel like I can't do it. It helps to talk about this shit—it really does.

— Jim R.,
serving time for dealing drugs and manslaughter

What Are Your Values?

➤ Look back at the list of traditional values on pages 57 and 58. Choose ten values that are important to you.

1. _____

2. _____

3. _____

4. _____

5. _____

6. _____

7. _____

8. _____

9. _____

10. _____

➤ In a separate notebook, use one page to write about each value. You should ask yourself the following questions:

- Why is this value important to me?

- How have I ignored or hurt this value while using or being locked up?

- How will I use this value to help me in my recovery?

You may still be working on exercise 25, Relationship History, from part 2. That exercise was designed to give you a deeper look into your value system. The next section on boundaries is closely linked to values. Setting boundaries is one way to make changes in your life. You use your values to help set and enforce boundaries.

Boundaries

Now we're going to build on what you've learned about boundaries in part 1.

What Are Healthy Boundaries?

Communication is a big part of healthy boundaries. Learning how to start conversations and make friends without letting people cross your emotional or physical boundaries is important. But being *too* guarded is trouble. We need balance. Remember when you first tried to ride a bike? Balance is difficult. But without it, you can't ride a bike. Balance with our boundaries is difficult, too. But without it, you can't build healthy relationships.

In part 1, you learned that boundaries have a purpose and help define who we are. We asked you to imagine a zipper on an invisible shield around your body. It could be unzipped for closeness with others or zipped up tightly for protection and withdrawal. We learned that people who grow up in addicted and abusive families are often confused about their boundaries.

Where are you today with your ability to hold your boundaries? Are you better able to keep yourself safe without having to blow up to make people keep their distance? While you are working on exercise 25, Relationship History, maybe you'll learn some things about how the people who took care of you maintained their boundaries.

Communication is a big part of healthy boundaries.

When you were young, was there someone (teacher, coach, grandparent, etc.) who did a good job of keeping his or her boundaries intact without blowing up? It's okay to have a role model even though you are now grown up. Boundary work is a long process. Staying sober is the first step toward establishing healthy boundaries.

Boundaries That Are Too Rigid

This exercise will help you identify boundaries that are too close and rigid.

EXAMPLE:

Bob is so worried that people will take advantage of him that he won't lend any money for lunch to his best friend who left his wallet at home.

➤ List three examples of when your boundaries were too rigid. If this isn't a problem for you, give examples of rigid boundaries that you have seen in others.

1. _____

_____

2. _____

_____

3. _____

_____

Boundaries That Are Too Loose

This exercise will help you identify boundaries that are too loose.

EXAMPLE:

Bill met a guy at the bar. When the guy told Bill he didn't have a place to stay, Bill let him spend the night even though Bill didn't know him. Bill's boundaries are too loose to protect him and his family.

➤ List three examples of when you were overly trusting and had boundaries that were too loose. If this isn't a problem for you, give examples of loose boundaries that you have seen in others.

1. _____

_____

2. _____

_____

3. _____

_____

If we don't set our own boundaries, others will set them for us. If we don't know what to think, others will do our thinking for us. If we don't know how to feel, others will tell us how they want us to feel or not feel. When we are not sure about our boundaries, our boundaries will not be clear to others.

Healthy Boundaries

This exercise will help you identify boundaries that are flexible and helpful.

EXAMPLE:

Ricardo sees a friend when he's out shopping with his wife. Ricardo's friend wants to borrow some money to buy a bottle. Ricardo says, "No man. The money I have in my pocket goes for my family, but you're still welcome to come by for coffee or just to hang out." Ricardo's boundaries are strong enough to protect his family and flexible enough to recognize that he still cares about his friend.

➤ List three examples of when your boundaries were flexible. If you haven't yet developed flexible boundaries, give three examples of what your boundaries will be like when you are healthier.

1. _____

   _____

2. _____

   _____

3. _____

   _____

Problem Solving

By setting healthy boundaries, problem solving won't be so difficult. Learning how to solve problems is essential to leading a satisfying life. You can use the seven steps of problem solving, listed below, with each of your problems.

In order to have a successful life, you need to solve your problems as they come up. Here, we've adapted Gary Smalley's seven steps to problem solving.

Seven Steps to Problem Solving

1. What's the problem?

2. What do you want to happen?

3. What are some possible solutions?
   What are the consequences of each solution?
   (*It is sometimes helpful to make a list of pros and cons for each possible solution. Talk your options over with someone who can help you identify realistic consequences and make healthy choices.*)

4. What's the best solution?

5. Try it!

6. Is it working?

7. If not, try something else.

Problem Solving
Using the Seven Steps

This exercise will help you use the seven steps of problem solving with your own problems. You will work on parts 1, 2, 3, and 4 of this exercise now. Your facilitator will tell you when to fill in parts 5, 6, and 7. Use a problem you are dealing with right now.

➤ 1. What's the problem?

> EXAMPLE:
>
> *"Somebody took my headphones."*

_____

_____

_____

_____

➤ 2. What do you want to happen?

> EXAMPLE:
>
> *"I just want my headphones back."*

_____

_____

_____

_____

"Life is a series of problems. Do you want to moan about them, or solve them?"

— M. Scott Peck,
The Road Less Traveled

➤ 3. What are some possible solutions?

EXAMPLE:

"Options include (a) busting someone's head open if I think he took my headphones and (b) asking my celly and members of my group if someone borrowed them."

_____

_____

_____

_____

_____

What are the consequences of each solution? Talk this over with someone.

EXAMPLE:

"If I bust someone's head open, I'm probably going to seg. I may get kicked out of this program and make more enemies and jeopardize my own safety. But if my celly has my headphones, I'll get them back. In group, I could let the others know the headphones are missing and ask them to return them to the officer at the front desk or some other location—no questions asked."

_____

_____

_____

_____

_____

_____

_____

➤ 4. What's the best solution?

    EXAMPLE:

    "If I bust someone's head open and go to seg,
    I still won't have my headphones back. Instead,
    I'll let the guys know that the headphones are
    missing and ask for them to be returned—no
    questions asked."

_____

_____

_____

_____

➤ 5. Try it!

    EXAMPLE:

    "I will give the guys in the group twenty-four
    hours to return the headphones."

_____

_____

_____

_____

➤ 6. Is it working?

EXAMPLE:

*"Did I get my headphones back or not? If not,
I will try another solution."*

_____

_____

_____

_____

➤ 7. If not, try something else.

EXAMPLE:

*"I'll talk to staff about it. After all, if I don't have
the headphones and they are on my property
list, I'll be the one in trouble."*

Learning how to
solve problems is
essential to leading
a satisfying life.

_____

_____

_____

_____

131

Dealing with Feelings

Many of our problems happen because we can't handle our emotions. ***Anger*** is an emotion that all of us can relate to. Although anger is often labeled as negative, it is not negative. It's what we do with this emotion that can produce negative results. For example, if we use our anger as an excuse to display ***hostility*** or ***aggression***, we are misusing that anger.

As we mentioned in part 2, the anger we show on the outside can be used to cover up our feelings on the inside. This especially applies to feelings we're uncomfortable with, such as sadness, loneliness, confusion, and fear. The illustration below shows seven emotions that can be covered up by anger.

ANGER AND THE SPECTRUM OF EMOTIONS

Many people who are recovering from alcohol and other drug abuse and criminal behaviors are angry. They have trouble coping with their anger. This might be a problem for you, too. Many people say they relapsed because they couldn't handle their anger in a positive way. Unchecked anger is a threat to society, your sobriety, and your relationships with other people.

Anger

Anger is an emotion that tells us something is wrong. You may want to fight back at the person or the event that you believe caused the feeling.

Hostility

Hostility is a negative attitude directed toward others. If hostility is used to intimidate someone, it may lead to aggression.

Aggression

Aggression is a behavior that harms and humiliates others. It comes out when we don't correctly deal with our anger and hostility.

Problems with anger can happen for several reasons. False pride and arrogance are big factors.

For some people, being angry with other people actually comes from being angry with themselves.

Maybe you have experienced this. Anger turned inward might be a result of problems addiction has caused in your life. You might direct your anger at others or blame them for your feelings. Or you might have learned to handle anger in ways that aren't healthy. For example, without taking time to think about it first, you might yell at somebody or pick a fight. You may keep all your anger inside, letting it slowly build up until you blow off steam by exploding at someone. Or your anger may be caused by not seeing the situation clearly. This usually happens to people who are easily provoked into feeling angry and who find many things or people to feel angry at.

It's time to look at your anger. Exercise 31 will help you understand more about your own anger.

Jim's Story

Okay, here's one way of looking at this. There are some guys you would love to play flag football with. While everybody else's flag is about a foot long, their flags (the things that piss them off) are about ten feet long! So, a guy way downfield can just put his foot down and our player gets sacked! That's how it was for me. All it took was for someone to look at me funny and I was ready to go at it. I didn't know that other people could tell how easy it was to get me going. After I did some work in treatment, I figured out that I could stop giving those guys the satisfaction of ticking me off.

— Jim R.,
serving time for dealing drugs and manslaughter

Assessing Your Anger

Answer the following questions as openly and as honestly as you can.

➤ What's your definition of anger?

> EXAMPLE:
>
> *"I think of anger as something that somebody else makes me feel."*

_____

_____

_____

➤ How often do you get angry?

> EXAMPLE:
>
> *"I know I get angry every day. Most days maybe a couple of times."*

_____

_____

_____

➤ What things anger you?

> EXAMPLE:
>
> *"The way other people act and the things they say."*

_____

_____

_____

_____

_____

_____

_____

_____

➤ How does your body react when you get angry?

EXAMPLE:

"I get headaches and I know I get red in the face."

_____

_____

_____

➤ When you get angry, are you able to listen to others or worry about the consequences of your behavior?

EXAMPLE:

"When I'm mad, I never want to hear what anyone else has to say."

_____

_____

_____

➤ How do you relieve your anger?

> EXAMPLE:
>
> *"I used to drink, drug, take it out on other people, and get in fights."*

_____

_____

_____

➤ Did your anger bring you behind bars? Why or why not?

> EXAMPLE:
>
> *"I know that me losing it is what brought me to this cell, but sometimes I still blame the system."*

_____

_____

_____

➤ Have relationships ended because of your anger?

> EXAMPLE:
>
> *"I know my girl would still be with me if I didn't blow up at her all the time. Sometimes my friends get sick of hearing me yell, too."*

_____

_____

_____

➤ What are some of the negatives to expressing anger in the way you usually do? What don't you like about the way you express your anger?

EXAMPLE:

"Sometimes I blow up about little shit and then feel like a complete fool."

_____

_____

➤ What are some of the benefits to expressing anger in the way you usually do? What do you like about the way you express your anger?

EXAMPLE:

"Sometimes it helps me push away people who are getting too close to me."

_____

_____

Many of our problems happen because we can't handle our emotions.

➤ How will managing your anger make your life different?

EXAMPLE:

"I think I could hold on to relationships better."

_____

_____

Hostile, angry feelings can be dangerous because they often lead to relapse. Anger can be just as addictive as alcohol or other drugs. It triggers the same brain chemical. Just like some other drugs, it feels good at the moment and blocks feelings of pain. Are you an anger junkie? Maybe at some point in your life, anger might have saved you. As you learned in part 2, it may have helped you cope with a troublesome childhood. But now, it's time to grow up and figure out better ways to deal with life.

The Positive and Negative Effects of Anger

Positive effects of anger	Negative effects of anger
• Gives you energy	• Gives you too much energy and makes you feel all wound up
• Helps you talk with others	• Some people will avoid you when they can tell you are angry
• Can motivate you to take control of your life	
• Can motivate you to take action to resolve a problem	• May make it difficult to think clearly and act responsibly
• Makes you feel in control over a situation	• Makes the problems you have bigger
• Makes you feel power over others	• Makes you look out of control
	• Makes others afraid of you

There's a direct connection between anger and abusing alcohol and other drugs. There are ways to deal with anger without covering it up and keeping it inside you until you explode. We'll teach you ways to deal effectively with your anger, not only inside the facility but also in the outside world.

Here are five tips that will help you deal better with your anger.

Tip 1: Recognize angry feelings.

Be aware of when you are angry. How does your anger show? Look for the anger clues, such as a headache, stomachache, or puffing yourself up. Other clues are in our heads, such as having revenge fantasies, planning on getting high, or feeling worthless. Finally, we have the action clues, such as arguing, getting physical, or avoiding people.

Tip 2: Identify situations that trigger your anger.

Be aware of what situations are likely to trigger your anger. When you are in the community, is it difficult for you to go shopping for groceries with the kids? Do you blow up when you are trying to fix something around the house? When you are broke, do you get ticked off easily? Pay attention to the situations that bother you.

Jack's Story

I never realized that anger was connected to my drinking. I always blamed it on everyone else. The only thing I can change is what I think about. I can't make other people do what I want for long. I drove myself crazy trying to control everyone and everything around me. And all it left me was more angry and frustrated.

— Jack S.,
serving time for dealing drugs and aggravated robbery

Tip 3: Identify what your anger does to you and other people.

Be aware of how you usually act when you get mad. For example, do you feel your heart beating really fast when you are angry? Do you notice that you feel hot and can't think clearly? Do other people look scared when you start to blow up? Pay attention to what happens to you and others.

Tip 4: Handle your anger.

Be aware that there are many different ways to handle your anger. For example, you can talk to the person who you are angry with, but only if you think you can hold it together while you talk. You can talk to someone else if you can't talk to the person you are angry with. You could do something physical, such as exercising.

Tip 5: Predict the future.

Be aware of your choices. Of the choices you have at this time, which is best? What will happen if you choose *a*? What will happen if you choose *b*? For example, if you are angry with your girl after you get off the phone, should you take it out on your celly? What will happen if you do? Should you go to the gym and try to work it off? What will happen if you do? Predict the best future for yourself.

Practice these tips, especially in situations where you're only feeling a little angry. It's those times when you'll be able to stay in control long enough to think about your options and try one. The more you do this, the easier it will be to think before you lose it. And then when more difficult situations come up, you'll be able to better deal with them, too.

If you still have difficulty handling anger after trying these tips, ask your counselor to help you find ways to deal with your anger.

Exercise 32 will help you put some of what you learned about your anger into action.

EXERCISE 32 EXERCISE

Your Anger Feelings

Each of the five tips for handling anger in a positive way will be used in this exercise.

1. Write down a situation when you got angry within the last twenty-four hours.

   EXAMPLE:

   "They shook down my cell yesterday."

   _____

   _____

   _____

   How did your body react?

   EXAMPLE:

   "My face got red and my head started pounding."

   _____

   _____

   _____

What kind of thoughts went through your head?

EXAMPLE:

"These guys are out to get me."

_____

_____

How did you behave?

EXAMPLE:

"I started arguing with the guards."

_____

_____

➤ 2. Write down a situation when you got angry within the last week.

_____

_____

_____

Hostile, angry feelings can be dangerous because they often lead to relapse.

➤ 3. Write down a situation when you got angry while you were out on the street.

_____

_____

_____

➤ 4. Look at the three situations you listed in questions 1, 2, and 3. Put the one that made you most angry after letter *c* below. Put the one that you were the least angry about under letter *a* below. Put the other one after letter *b*.

a. a little angry

_____

_____

b. angry

_____

_____

c. very angry

_____

_____

Who else was involved in each of these situations?

a. _____

_____

b. _____

_____

c. _____

_____

What set you off in each of these situations?

a. _____

b. _____

c. _____

EXERCISE **33** EXERCISE

Identify Triggers
of Your Anger

➤ List four things you say to other people when you are angry.

EXAMPLE:

"You can't treat me that way."

Other examples might include
- "You think you are better than me, don't you?"
- "I'll show you who is boss!"
- "What were you thinking?"

1. _____

_____

2. _____

_____

3. _____

_____

4. _____

_____

➤ List four things that you say to yourself when you are
angry.

EXAMPLE:

"No one understands me."

1. _____

   _____

2. _____

   _____

3. _____

   _____

4. _____

   _____

Other examples might include
- "Everyone thinks they are better than me."
- "Everyone treats me badly because they think I don't matter."
- "Everybody is out for themselves."

Jim's Story

The thing that surprised me the most was all the stuff I've been saying to myself that pissed me off. I always thought it was other people and what they said and did. But I was doing a lot of it on my own. It was weird to hear the other guys talking about how I looked to them when I got pissed off. Sometimes it's hard to listen, but this is stuff we need to know.

— Jim R.,
serving time for dealing drugs and manslaughter

Everything that we've covered in this workbook on the topic of anger can be helpful to you. Taking an inventory is always helpful. We talked about taking a personal inventory in part 2. Now we are talking about taking an anger inventory. At the end of the day, complete an "anger log." It's easy. It involves five questions that you should ask yourself each time you become angry. They are

1. What is the situation?

2. What angry thoughts did you have?

3. What did you do?

4. What should you have done?

5. What are calming thoughts you could use to replace the angry thoughts?

Do this anger log at the end of each day and then bring it to class. The purpose of this exercise is to learn more about your anger and how to replace angry thoughts with calming thoughts. By doing an anger log each day, you will learn more about your patterns of anger.

Getting Through to Other People

A real key to controlling anger is being able to talk to other people. This means the better you are able to tell someone how you feel or what's on your mind, the less chance you have of losing control.

Next, we will spell out the difference between being assertive and being aggressive. It's like the difference between doing the right thing and doing the wrong thing!

Even though you've lost a lot of privileges while being incarcerated, you can still be in charge of your own life. The key to being in charge is knowing how to communicate.

Communication Styles

The four main styles of communicating are

1. **Passive**

   This means being unwilling to say clearly what you want or need. It means hoping that someone will guess what you want.

   EXAMPLE:

   Calling home and wanting to talk to your dad, but not telling your mom, just talking to her hoping that she'll figure out you want to talk to your dad, too.

2. **Aggressive**

   This means taking what you want, by force if necessary. It means demanding rather than discussing.

   EXAMPLE:

   Calling up and demanding to talk to your dad.

3. **Passive-aggressive**

   This means looking like you are harmless, but setting people up at the same time.

   EXAMPLE:

   You call home and want to talk to your dad, but you don't tell your mom that. Instead, you talk to your brother later and say that your mom wouldn't let you talk to your dad.

4. **Assertive**

   This means being able to figure out what you want and then asking for it in a nonthreatening manner.

   EXAMPLE:

   You call home and want to talk to your dad, so you ask your mom to put him on the phone.

A real key to controlling anger is being able to talk to other people.

No one uses just one style, but most people use one style more often than others. As you read the definitions of each style, try to see yourself in the examples. What is your most common style? Is it helpful for you? Do you need to learn better communication skills?

Passive Style

When you communicate passively, you try to avoid conflict and confrontation with others at all costs. This means you often put your personal beliefs and rights aside to go along with someone else. You don't talk about your feelings, wants, and needs. You may think that this doesn't cause any harm because you're not upsetting anyone, but that's not true. This style lowers your self-esteem and leaves your needs unmet. You then feel ignored, and resentments can build up.

Signs of passive communication include

- not looking people in the eyes

- not showing much expression in voice or face

- speaking quietly

- never sounding upset

- not saying what you really think

- often using words such as *maybe, probably, kind of,* and *I suppose*

- smoothing over problems with apologies

Do you know any passive people? Have you ever been irritated by someone who never asked for what he wanted? Do you see yourself in this style?

Aggressive Style

When you communicate aggressively, you put yourself first and ignore the rights of others. You don't pay attention to others' feelings, wants, or needs—but you demand that yours be heard and met. You will do almost anything to get what you want, even if it means controlling and manipulating others. Although you might get what you want, you're not always happy with the result. When we force people to give us what we want, we don't get the same feelings as when people give to us because they care.

Signs of aggressive communication include

- speaking with a loud voice or unfriendly tone
- using lots of profanity
- glaring or mean-mugging
- standing close to the person to intimidate
- showing feelings by slamming doors, hitting, or throwing things
- focusing on the faults of others
- demanding what you want when you want it
- criticizing and giving advice, but not listening to others

Do you know any aggressive people? Have you ever been irritated by someone who always demanded what he wanted? Do you see yourself in this style?

You will do almost anything to get what you want, even if it means controlling and manipulating others.

Passive-Aggressive Style

When you communicate passive-aggressively, you violate the rights of others (aggressive style) while trying to look like you are putting the other person's rights first (passive style). You seem concerned about others' feelings and needs, but will only act on them if they meet your own feelings, wants, and needs. You don't tell others what you want or need; you expect them to guess. You do this to control and manipulate (like the aggressive person) and to avoid direct conflict (like the passive person).

Signs of passive-aggressive communication include

- rolling your eyes, but denying anything's wrong

- using sarcasm and aggressive statements but saying it's just a joke

- saying yes when you're not planning to follow through

- giving dishonest feedback to humiliate or set up the other person

Do you know any passive-aggressive people? Have you ever been irritated by someone who never clearly asked for what he wanted? Do you see yourself in this style?

Assertive Style

When you communicate assertively, you "okay" your rights and the rights of others. You express your feelings, wants, and needs openly and with respect. You're open to hearing others express their feelings and needs—and you're willing to compromise. You keep a balance between giving, taking, and asking for help. You act in your own best interest without trying to make others uncomfortable. This style helps relationships last longer. It builds strong self-esteem, self-respect, and self-confidence.

Signs of assertive communication include

- direct eye contact without staring

- relaxed body

- facial expressions that match how you feel and what you're saying

- expressing feelings, opinions, and needs as they come up (if appropriate)

- taking responsibility for actions and avoiding blaming others

- being a good listener who gives direct and honest comments

- taking responsibility for feelings and opinions with such comments as "I feel afraid when . . ." or "I feel angry when . . ."

Do you know any assertive people? Have you ever admired someone who knew how to ask for help openly? Do you see yourself in this style?

Identifying Communication Styles

Keep in mind the four communication styles (passive, aggressive, passive-aggressive, and assertive) as you respond to these two situations.

Situation A

You are saving a space for a friend in class. This guy sits down next to you without asking whether the seat is taken. What do you say? Do not use the same answers that are listed in the examples.

▶ **Aggressive response**

> EXAMPLE:
>
> *You say, "Get away from that chair before I bash you in the head with it."*

_____

_____

_____

▶ **Passive response**

> EXAMPLE:
>
> *You say nothing at all. When your friend comes back, you let him handle it.*

_____

_____

_____

➤ **Passive-aggressive response**

EXAMPLE:

You say, "You can sit there if you want, but when my friend comes back, I wouldn't want to be you."

_____

_____

_____

➤ **Assertive response**

EXAMPLE:

You say, "My friend was sitting there. Would you mind sitting in a different chair?"

_____

_____

_____

Situation B

You just finished treatment and were released from incarceration. A friend who's been in Alcoholics Anonymous (AA) for many years invites you to an AA meeting. You go with him, but after you get there, he leaves you to go talk to other people. You're uncomfortable and don't know anyone else there. What do you say or do? Do not use the same answers that are listed in the examples.

➤ **Aggressive response**

EXAMPLE:

You leave the meeting, and when you hear from your friend, you cuss him out for not sticking by you.

_____

_____

_____

➤ **Passive response**

EXAMPLE:

You stay right where you are. You don't talk to anyone else. You just feel more and more worried. When your friend comes back, he says, "Sorry I was gone so long. Were you okay?" You just nod your head like you are fine.

_____

_____

_____

➤ **Passive-aggressive response**

> EXAMPLE:
>
> *You stay right where you are. You don't talk to anyone else. You just feel more and more worried. When your friend comes back, he says, "Sorry I was gone so long. Were you okay?" You say, "Of course I'm fine. Anyone ten days out of the joint in a room full of strangers feels great!"*

_____

_____

_____

➤ **Assertive response**

> EXAMPLE:
>
> *You follow your friend. When you see him, you wave, walk up to him, and say, "Mind if I hang with you? I don't know any of these other people."*

_____

_____

_____

Did the exercise above help you learn a little bit more about the different styles of communication? Don't forget to ask other people how they see you because sometimes we don't see ourselves clearly.

Identifying Your Communication Style

➤ Think again about the four communication styles. Circle the style you use most often.

1. passive

2. aggressive

3. passive-aggressive

4. assertive

➤ Write down two situations when you used the communication style you circled.

1. _____

_____

2. _____

_____

Even though that may be your most common communication style, you use different styles with different people. For example, you might appear very passive with your PO and very aggressive with your former partner.

Evaluate your communication style as it relates to the counselors versus men in your treatment program. For example, do you find yourself being passive with the counselor just because you know what he or she wants to hear? And do you find yourself being aggressive with other guys just to keep them off your back?

Identifying Personal Trouble Spots

➤ In this exercise, list three people or groups of people that you have the most difficulty asserting yourself with (for example, someone in your group, your partner, your boss, a using friend). What communication style do you usually use when talking with these people?

Person	Usual style of communication
1.	
2.	
3.	

➤ Next, list the three topics or situations that you find most difficult or uncomfortable to talk about (for example, your fears, your failures, your worries about recovery or using). Then tell what style you use when talking about these things.

Topic/Situation	Usual style of communication
1.	
2.	
3.	

➤ If you don't make any changes in your communication style, what will happen to your recovery?

_____

_____

_____

➤ Write two ways that learning to communicate assertively can improve your chances for a successful recovery.

1. _____

_____

2. _____

_____

Jack's Story

Dude! Don't ignore this stuff about communication styles. I always liked to stand toe-to-toe with the other guy. When he backed down, I felt like I had won. But what did I win? I know I need to be able to say what I want without flying off the handle. More than that, I need to be able to handle it when I don't get what I want.

— Jack S.,
serving time for dealing drugs and aggravated robbery

"I" Messages and "You" Messages

Aggressive communicators often use "you" messages and assertive communicators often use "I" messages. What's the difference? When you use "I" messages, you take responsibility for your feelings, thoughts, and actions. You use the words *I, me,* or *my.* When you use "you" messages, you put the responsibility for your feelings, thoughts, and actions on others.

EXAMPLE:

You get home and your son hasn't done the chores he'd agreed to do.

"You" message:

"You make me so mad when you don't do your work. You need to do it now or you're not going to the movie."

"I" message:

"I feel angry when you don't do your chores as you said you would. I want you to do them before dinner, or you can't go to the movie."

In the first example, you give your son responsibility for your anger—and that also makes it his responsibility to fix it. You then demand that he does what you want using another "you" statement.

In the second example, you take responsibility for your anger and talk about your son's behavior. This lets you deal with your anger, even if your son's behavior doesn't change. Finally, you tell him what will happen if he does not follow through.

The goal is to communicate assertively. This means using "I" statements instead of "you" statements. This is a difficult concept. But there's a formula for communicating assertively on the next page.

Here's the assertiveness formula:

I feel _____

when you _____

because _____ .

I want/need _____ .

If this formula looks confusing, don't worry. We're going to explain it in detail.

Step 1: I feel . . .

It's easy to confuse what you think and what you feel. When you want to name a feeling, remember that feelings are described by one word, such as happy, nervous, worried, or excited.

EXAMPLES:

I feel worried

not

I think you're making a mistake

———

I feel hurt

not

I think you're trying to hurt me

Step 2: when you . . .

Here you need to name the action you want to talk about rather than make general statements.

EXAMPLES:

when you don't attend your meeting

not

when you give up on AA

———

when you say I'm lazy

not

when you're being a jerk

Step 3: because . . .

Here you focus on the effect of the action on the relationship. This step applies mostly to people you're close to.

EXAMPLES:

because it may be a relapse sign

not

because I said so

———

because it seems disrespectful to me

not

because I hate you

Step 4: I want/need . . .

Here you talk about your wants and needs. Again, you use "I" messages and talk about the behavior in step 2.

EXAMPLES:

I would like you to keep going to meetings because your recovery is important to me.

not

You have to go to meetings or I will call your PO.

———

I need you to stop calling me names and to be respectful.

not

You never say the right thing.

Using the Assertiveness Formula

➤ **Situation 1:**

You're with your best friend. He says, "I know you can't get a dirty UA, but you're my best friend and I can't have my birthday bash without you." When you tell him you won't drink with him, he says, "What? Are you too good for all your old friends now?" Fill in how you would respond using the assertiveness formula.

I feel

_____

when you

_____

_____

because

_____

_____

I want/need

_____

_____

_____

➤ **Situation 2:**

You and your significant other go to her friend's house. Her co-workers are there. One of them makes a sarcastic comment because you aren't drinking. Everybody laughs. Fill in how you would respond using the assertiveness formula.

I feel

_____

when you

_____

_____

because

_____

_____

I want/need

_____

_____

_____

➤ **Situation 3:**

Your partner says, "Haven't you done that yet? I knew I should have done it myself!" Fill in how you would respond using the assertiveness formula.

I feel

_____

when you

_____

_____

because

_____

_____

I want/need

_____

_____

_____

Now, think of two situations you've been in during the last few days. Describe the situation and then fill in how you would respond using the assertiveness formula.

➤ **Situation 1:**

_____

_____

_____

I feel

_____

when you

_____

_____

because

_____

_____

I want/need

_____

_____

_____

▶ **Situation 2:**

_____

_____

_____

I feel

_____

when you

_____

_____

because

_____

_____

I want/need

_____

_____

_____

It's not easy to learn to be assertive. A communication style is kind of like being right-handed or left-handed. It just feels natural. When we practice being assertive, we often feel clumsy, like we don't know what to say next. But after a while, we can learn new ways of communicating. After all, you have come this far, so don't give up now.

Empathy

Empathy is the ability to understand what someone else is experiencing. It's not a *feeling,* it's a *skill* that can be learned and strengthened.

People learn empathy from the inside out. That means we need to pay attention to what is going on with *us* before we can understand what's going on with someone else. We need to be aware of our own thoughts and feelings—even the ones that are uncomfortable.

We need to be able to see ourselves clearly before we can see others.

Alcohol and other drugs kept us blind to our own experiences and distorted our experiences. Maybe you said things like "they'll get over it" when you thought about your victims. Maybe you said that so you would not have to put yourself in their shoes. Empathy is about doing just that: putting yourself in their shoes, on purpose.

The more you are willing to do this, the less likely you are to make more victims. No more victims means no more time behind bars. If you have been locked up long enough, if you are sick and tired of being sick and tired, if you want to be back with your family, use these exercises to help you develop your empathy.

We need to pay attention to what is going on with us before we can understand what's going on with someone else.

Know What Blocks You

Here are some common blocks that people use to avoid empathy.

> **Denial:** "I didn't do it."
>
> **Victim stance:** "I had to do it."
>
> **Minimizing:** "I did it, but it's not that bad."
>
> **Blaming:** "They made me do it."
>
> **Delusion:** "I never hurt anyone."
>
> **Dehumanizing:** "She was just a ho."
>
> **Conning:** "I'll say I'm sorry so they get off my back."
>
> **Shame:** "I'm a monster for what I did."

➤ Select two blocks from the list above that you use, and write about how you use them. It's okay if this makes you uncomfortable.

> EXAMPLES:
>
> *"I use denial. My mother still thinks they got the wrong guy. I don't even know if I would have the guts to admit the truth."*
>
> *"I use victim stance. I told everyone I had to sell drugs to feed my children. I acted like a victim of the system."*

1. I use _____

   _____

   _____

2. I use _____

_____

_____

➤ Now, for each of the blocks you chose, put yourself in your victim's shoes.

EXAMPLES:

"I heard that the guy I shot is still in a wheelchair. He can't even get out of his house on his own. His whole life has changed because of what I did."

"My kids didn't see much of me on the street. When they did, I was high. They must think I abandoned them."

1. _____

_____

_____

_____

2. _____

_____

_____

_____

Yes, You Can!

Maybe you have said that you could not understand what your victims went through because the same thing never happened to you. If you want to develop your empathy skills you need to remember this: pain is pain. That means that even if you never experienced *exactly* the same thing, you have experienced something like it.

➤ Describe one of your offenses as if you were the victim. Be specific. Write about the victim's thoughts and feelings, and how the victim was affected. Don't try to avoid the uncomfortable feelings. Use your notebook if you need more space to write.

EXAMPLE:

"I was waiting for the bus. He came up behind me and put his hand on my mouth. He said he had a knife. I was really scared. I thought he was going to kill me. He cut the strap on my purse and shoved me to the ground. I kept thinking he was going to stab me. He grabbed my purse and ran away. I was scared to go home because he had my address and my keys. I couldn't sleep. I still have nightmares. I still wonder why he picked me."

_____

_____

_____

_____

_____

_____

_____

_____

 EXERCISE **40** EXERCISE

Practice, Practice, Practice!

We gain new skills through practice. There are many ways to practice empathy. Notice when someone is upset, put yourself in his or her shoes, and say and do what you wish would happen for you.

➤ Give three examples of showing empathy this week.

EXAMPLE:

Helping someone with an assignment.

1. _____

   _____

2. _____

   _____

3. _____

   _____

Compassion

Compassion grows out of empathy. With compassion, we not only put ourselves in someone else's shoes, we do it with understanding, acceptance, and forgiveness.

It is not enough simply to know what someone else is experiencing. We must be able to understand how he or she got there. We must be able to accept that person just as he or she is. We must be able to forgive the bad choices that person made.

Compassion is also something that grows from the inside out. Are you compassionate to yourself? This does not mean bluffing, or pretending, that you think everything you have done is okay. It means separating *who* you are from *what* you have done.

It means recognizing that you have had your own pain and loss.

Do you understand and accept yourself where you are? This does not mean accepting what you did. Again, it means separating who you are from what you have done.

Can you forgive your bad choices? This does not mean blaming other people for your own bad choices. It means separating who you are from the bad choices you have made.

You can't shame yourself into being the man you want to be. Having tender feelings about yourself will help you to be more gentle with others as well.

Compassion comes from *feeling* our pain, and *deciding* not to give that pain to other people. Compassion comes from noticing other people's pain, and deciding that their pain is like our own pain.

Alcohol and other drugs hide our pain from us. When we are numb to our own pain, we are also numb to the pain we cause others. The following exercises will help you to remember the pain you have hidden from yourself.

Alcohol and other drugs hide our pain from us.

Where Did All the Pain Go?

➤ Think back to a time when you were using and disappointed someone who cared about you. It might have been a parent or foster parent, a girlfriend or spouse, a child or younger brother or sister. Write a paragraph about what happened. Be specific, even if it's painful. Use your notebook if you need more space to write.

EXAMPLE:

"I remember one time when I promised my daughter I wouldn't drink anymore. She was only six. I told her I quit, but I was still drinking. I thought I could fool her. She used to smell the Coke I was drinking to see if it smelled 'funny.' I opened the trunk, and she saw the bottle of whiskey. She didn't say a word, she just looked at me. I felt ashamed."

_____

_____

_____

_____

_____

_____

_____

_____

➤ Now write about what you did to get away from the painful feelings.

EXAMPLE:

"I got mad at my daughter and her mother. Even though I knew I was the one with the problem, I blamed it on them. I slapped my daughter because I couldn't stand the look on her face. I took off and got really drunk, then I robbed a liquor store. I was relieved to get to jail—so I didn't have to see those looks anymore."

_____

_____

_____

_____

_____

EXERCISE **42** EXERCISE

Turning the Tables on Shame

To feel compassion for other people, we need compassion for ourselves. When we think of how we have hurt others, it's easy for us to feel ashamed. Shame keeps us prisoners, even when we are no longer behind bars.

Guilt is the remedy. Shame tells us we are worthless, useless, and *bad*. Guilt reminds us that what we did was wrong, but we can make it right by making amends and choosing to act differently.

➤ Think of an action that makes you feel ashamed. Describe it in detail below. Use your notebook if you need more space to write.

EXAMPLE:

"I was on the run from my PO. I knew that my granddad's car was on the street, and his spare keys were under the seat. I took his car, even though I knew he couldn't get to work without it. I drove to another state and traded the car for some dope. Every time I think about what I did, I feel like shit. He wrote to me, but I feel too rotten to write back to him. He doesn't even know what I did."

_____

_____

_____

_____

_____

_____

_____

_____

_____

_____

_____

➤ Now imagine ignoring your shame and facing up to your guilt. What could you do differently?

EXAMPLE:

"I could face up to the truth and write to him. I know he is going to be very angry and disappointed in me. But at least I'll be able to talk to him before it's too late."

_____

_____

_____

_____

_____

_____

_____

_____

_____

Take some time to think about actions you can take to heal your old relationships. It will not be easy, but the relationships that can handle the truth will be stronger for it.

Grief and Loss

One thing you can do to help yourself be more compassionate is to look at grief and loss.

Grief is the collection of feelings and actions that come up for us when we lose something important. Alcohol and other drugs helped us to hide from our grief.

Many men also use anger and violence to hide their grief from others. Grief does not just come from the death of a loved one. Some other common areas of grief and loss are covered in exercise 43.

 EXERCISE 43 EXERCISE

43a.
Loss of Material Goods

This is the loss of things that have been important to us. Things are important for many reasons. Sometimes we use things as a cushion to protect us from our shame. For example, you may have used jewelry, cars, and clothes to convince yourself that what you were doing was okay—even if you knew that it was not. You may have used money to try to buy friends—so you would not feel lonely. You may have used a fancy house to try to fool people about the double life you lived. Some things that we have lost are important only to us—like a photograph of someone we cared about.

➤ What are some important things that you have lost? How did you feel about your loss? How did you avoid your feelings?

EXAMPLE:

"I lost my truck when I got locked up. I couldn't make the payments and it got repossessed. I loved that truck because it made me feel like I owned the road. I was sad when it was gone, and ashamed that I couldn't make the payments. I blamed my ex and threatened her over the phone. All that got me was divorce papers."

_____

_____

_____

_____

_____

_____

_____

_____

_____

_____

43b.
Loss of a Job

Losing a job can be a major loss for many people. You might have lost a job that gave you good feelings about yourself when it was discovered that you had taken money or property. You might have also lost face in the eyes of your family or friends. Losing a job is also about losing a role in life. For example, if you have ever had a job that gave you a feeling of power over other people (like dealing drugs), losing that job means losing that power. Once you're locked up, your powerlessness is more obvious than ever.

➤ Have you lost a job or role that was important to you? How did you feel? How did you hide your feelings from others?

EXAMPLE:

"My job was being a super-jock. I was the best basketball player in my school. All the teachers knew my name. I got away with lots of stuff. My mom and dad were proud of me. But I was doing speed and selling it to the other jocks. When I got busted, I became like a bum, a nobody. I'm sad about what I lost, especially the chance to go to college. I pretend like I don't care, but it still hurts."

Losing a job is also about losing a role in life.

_____

_____

_____

_____

_____

43c.
Losses of the Physical Self

This type of loss is about what our bodies have gone through. They can be simple losses such as losing a tooth in a fight, or complicated losses such as finding out we have HIV or hepatitis. Our body is the only thing we will ever own. Physical losses make us distrust who we are. They leave us feeling vulnerable and confused.

➤ Have you ever had this kind of loss? How did you feel? How did you hide your feelings?

EXAMPLE:

"I was in a fight with a guy and his buddy hit me with a pool cue. It knocked me out. After I came to, I was throwing up. Then later, I passed out again. Nobody knew it then, but I got brain damage. I tried to hide it from people because I was ashamed. Now I need help to do things I used to do on my own. I clown around and act dumb. But really, I'm scared and sad."

_____

_____

_____

_____

_____

_____

43d.
Loss of Control

Nobody likes to admit that they have lost control. But look around you. If you had control of your life, is this where you would be? If you are addicted to alcohol or other drugs, you have lost control of being able to predict how much you will use. If you have an addiction to gambling, you have lost control of how much money you will lose. Loss of control makes us feel weak, so we fight to pretend we still have control.

➤ Have you experienced loss of control? How did you feel? How did you hide your feelings from others?

> EXAMPLE:
>
> *"I knew that I couldn't control my alcohol use after I got too drunk to go to my mother's funeral. I was so disgusted with myself that I tried to commit suicide. A friend found me and took me to a hospital. After they let me out, I kept on drinking. I told people I could stop whenever I wanted to—but I knew I couldn't. It scared me to death, but I hid it by being a jerk and driving everyone away."*

_____

_____

_____

_____

_____

How do you deal with your loss of freedom?

43e.
Loss of Personal Freedom

Being locked up means an end to freedom. Every day, people on the outside get into their cars and drive wherever they want to go. Families get together and share a meal. Men and women dance and flirt and make love. Other men go out and fish or hunt, or play a game of catch with their children.

➤ How do you deal with your loss of freedom? How do you feel? How do you hide your feelings?

EXAMPLE:

"Every time I get locked up again, I shake down everybody I know to send me money. I meet up with guys I've known from before to watch my back. I lift weights and bulk up. I tell everybody this ain't nothing to cry about. Inside, I feel hopeless and scared. I act tough and get into fights so no one will know how I feel."

_____

_____

_____

_____

_____

_____

_____

43f.
Loss of Relationships

Everyone has had to deal with breakups. Many times we don't want to admit that we've been hurt, so we just play it off. Sometimes we decide that we won't ever get hurt if we just don't care about the person we're with. The problem with that is the relationship is never going to satisfy us. So maybe we get in two or three relationships at once. But we still find that we're lonely and thinking about "the one that got away."

➤ Have you lost relationships? How did you feel? How did you hide your feelings from other people?

EXAMPLE:

"I was really crazy about this one girl. I didn't want her to know how much I liked her so I didn't treat her very well. After a while, she dumped me. I couldn't really blame her. I pretended that I had dumped her and hooked up with one of her friends. I talked bad about her to everyone I knew. I still miss her."

_____

_____

_____

_____

_____

_____

43g.
Loss of Childhood

Many people lose their childhood while they are still children. Maybe someone who's supposed to take care of them hurts them. Many children are physically, emotionally, or sexually abused. They grow up too fast, and lose out on the things that every child should have.

➤ Did you experience painful losses in childhood? How did you feel? How did you hide your feelings from other people?

EXAMPLE:

"My mother is an alcoholic. For as long as I can remember, I had to take care of her. I never knew what she would do. I was afraid other kids would find out about her, so I never brought anyone home. I hated her, and I felt sorry for her. I pretended that I had a great childhood, because it was too painful to admit what really happened."

Many people lose their childhood while they are still children.

_____

_____

_____

_____

_____

_____

_____

Looking at painful issues can help you stay free. This is because avoiding pain only works for as long as we stay high or keep lying to ourselves. Looking honestly at the pain of our losses strengthens us. Looking at our pain without using alcohol or other drugs shows us we can accept life as it is—without running away.

Conclusion

You have come to the end of this workbook. We hope that you have learned some useful tools to help you get out and stay out.

We hope that you have made the decision to live clean and sober. If you have, you have a better chance of staying out.

We know that the ideas that you are hearing about are not easy to understand. We know that it's not easy to make changes, but it can be done. Some men have left confinement and never come back. You can be one of those men if you choose to be.

Jim's Story

Congratulations! You made it all the way through. I know I didn't think I could make it this far when I started. I'm glad you stuck it out. I hope you didn't just bullshit your way through 'cause if you did, you're the only one it's gonna hurt. Take care of yourself. I'll see you on the outs.

— Jim R.,
serving time for dealing drugs and manslaughter

Movie Resources

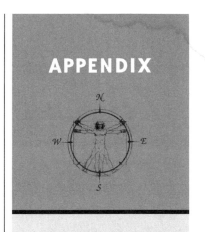

1. Boundaries

- *What's Love Got to Do with It* (1993)
  Deals with abusive relationships.

- *A River Runs through It* (1992)
  Deals with family expectations and rigid boundaries.

2. Childhood

- *The Great Santini* (1979)
  Deals with emotional, physical, and sexual abuse as well as issues of substance abuse.

- *Stand by Me* (1986)
  Deals with death, friends, support systems, and parent/child relationships.

- *This Boy's Life* (1993)
  Deals with emotional, physical, and sexual abuse; friends and support systems; and substance abuse.

3. Communication

- *Forrest Gump* (1994)
  Deals with communication and how to deal with disabilities.

- *Regarding Henry* (1991)
  Deals with communication and conflict resolution.

4. Culture

- *Mask* (1985)
  Deals with the biker subculture and how to deal with disabilities.

- *Soul Food* (1997)
  Deals with cultural values, traditions, and family relationships.

5. Personal Inventory

- *Clean and Sober* (1988)
  Deals with addiction and maintaining abstinence.

6. Family and Genetics

- *When a Man Loves a Woman* (1994)
  Deals with substance abuse and its impact on the family system.

- *Bang the Drum Slowly* (1973)
  Deals with friends and support systems as well as illness and disabilities.

- *Rain Man* (1988)
  Deals with family and understanding severe emotional illness.

7. Grief and Loss

- *Terms of Endearment* (1983)
  Deals with communication, conflict resolution, chronic illness, death and dying, and family-of-origin issues.

- *Fearless* (1993)
  Deals with emotional and affective disorders, chronic illness, and death and dying.

- *Ordinary People* (1980)
  Deals with adolescence, death and dying, conflict resolution, divorce, and emotional and affective disorders.

8. Intimacy

- *Philadelphia* (1993)
  Deals with a healthy intimate relationship in the midst of illness and prejudice.

- *Cocoon* (1985)
  Deals with friends and intimate support systems.

9. Parenting

- *On Golden Pond* (1981)
  Deals with family-of-origin issues and parent/child relationships.

- *Parenthood* (1989)
  Deals with family-of-origin issues and parenting (humorous).

10. Relationships

- *The Big Chill* (1983)
  Deals with friends and support systems.

- *Awakenings* (1990)
  Deals with relationships in the face of chronic illness.

11. Shame

- *The Graduate* (1967)
  Deals with the transition into adulthood, conflict resolution, and values and ethics.

- *Rudy* (1993)
  Deals with resolution in the face of shame—an inspiring look at a challenging subject.

12. Values

- *Chariots of Fire* (1981)
  Deals with traditional values being placed ahead of personal gain.

- *Quiz Show* (1994)
  Deals with giving up traditional values for personal gain.

APPENDIX

Sources

Clarke, Jean Illsley. *Connections: The Threads That Strengthen Families.* Center City, Minn.: Hazelden, 1999.

Coleman, Eli. *Chemical Dependency and Intimacy Dysfunction.* New York: Haworth Press, 1988.

Hesley, John W., and Jan G. Hesley. *Rent Two Films and Let's Talk in the Morning: Using Popular Movies in Psychotherapy.* New York: John Wiley & Sons, 1998.

Mason, Marilyn. *Intimacy.* Center City, Minn.: Hazelden, 1986.

O'Neil, Mike S., and Charles E. Newbold. *Boundary Power: How I Treat You, How I Let You Treat Me, How I Treat Myself.* Antioch, Tex.: Sonlight Publishing, Inc., 1998.

Peck, M. Scott. *The Road Less Traveled.* New York: Simon and Schuster, 1997.

Potter-Efron, Ronald, and Patricia Potter-Efron. *Letting Go of Shame: Understanding How Shame Affects Your Life.* Center City, Minn.: Hazelden, 1996.

Prochaska, James O., John C. Norcross, and Carlo C. DiClemente. *Changing for Good.* New York: Avon Books, 1995.

Schaeffer, Brenda. *Signs of Healthy Love.* Center City, Minn.: Hazelden, 1986.

Smalley, Gary. *Keys to Loving Relationships.* Branson, Mo.: Today's Family, 1998.

Substance Abuse and Crime. A Hazelden Research Update. Center City, Minn.: Hazelden, 2000.

Swanson, Jan, and Alan Cooper. *Coping with Emotional and Physical High-Risk Factors.* Center City, Minn.: Hazelden, 1994.

Thompson, Peg. *Finding Your Own Spiritual Path: An Everyday Guidebook.* Center City, Minn.: Hazelden, 1994.

Wanberg, Kenneth, and Harvey Milkman. *Criminal Conduct and Substance Abuse Treatment: Strategies for Self-Improvement and Change.* Thousand Oaks, Calif.: SAGE Publications, Inc., 1998.

Welo, Beverly. *Life beyond Loss: A Workbook for Incarcerated Men.* Lanham, Md.: American Correctional Association, 1995.

———. *Tough Customers: Counseling Unwilling Clients.* Lanham, Md.: American Correctional Association, 2001.

White, William L. *Pathways: From the Culture of Addiction to the Culture of Recovery.* Center City, Minn.: Hazelden, 1996.

NOTES

NOTES